Rosa

PERCHANCE
TO MARRY

by

CELINE CONWAY

HARLEQUIN   BOOKS

Winnipeg • Canada   New York • New York

PERCHANCE TO MARRY

First published in 1961 by Mills & Boon Limited,
50 Grafton Way, Fitzroy Square, London, England.

Harlequin Canadian edition published March, 1966
Harlequin U.S. edition published May, 1971

Standard Book Number: 373-52996-1.

Printed in Canada

CHAPTER ONE

VIOLA SHEPPARD remained in the taxi while Sally made the enquiries. She clasped her small gloved hands very tightly and made a conscious effort to prevent her thin delicate lips from pursing; no woman over the age of thirty should pleat her mouth, and Viola sorrowfully admitted, though not to outsiders, to being forty-seven. Not only forty-seven but a widow with a daughter of nineteen. Nineteen! And it seemed no time at all since she herself was climbing out of her gay teens into her even more exciting twenties. Life was so unfair.

This horrible taxi smelled of dust and cachous and garlic. The street was appallingly narrow and slummy, and could not possibly be the *avenida* they were looking for. But Sally said she had seen the name chopped out of the black stone building at the corner, and now she had stopped the taxi and got out to investigate. She seemed to have vanished into one of the dark doorways, and Viola wondered, sinkingly, what she would do if Sally didn't appear again.

They should never have come to Barcelona; she knew that now. It had sounded so marvellous in England: "Manageress required for beauty emporium which caters exclusively for English-speaking clients. Good salary and flat provided." Sally had tried to dissuade her from answering the advertisement, but she, Viola, had known that what she most needed was the warmth and highly romantic flavor of the Mediterranean.

She'd consulted their old friend, Dr. Mowbray. "You've been telling me I need a holiday in the south of France, but you also know I couldn't afford it. Barcelona may not have quite the atmosphere you prescribed, but I do know it a little. It's sunny and gay, and would give me a tremendous boost. I do have to find a post of some sort, and this one seems heaven-sent, if I can get it."

The doctor had looked dubious. "You'd take Sally, I suppose?"

"Yes, of course."

"She's just starting her second year at St. Alun's. She won't want to give it up."

"If they employ English beauty consultants they'll take an English nurse, I suppose. After all, the English-speaking people out there are bound to get ill sometimes."

"Couldn't you two manage a month's holiday at Biarritz, or somewhere?"

Forlornly, she had told him, "It wouldn't be enough. If I stay here in England I'll never recover from Richard's death. I depended on him for everything, and now, even though it's nearly a year since I lost him, I feel quite adrift. The winter has been so cold and wet and I've hardly been able to get out at all. Don't you think the climate of southern Spain would be good for me?"

"Of course it would; even thinking about it seems to have built you up a little. But I don't like to think of Sally being wrenched away from St. Alun's."

Viola had felt quite neglected and pettish. "Young people love change, and to travel. After a few months in Barcelona I may be able to do without her. Then she could come back and complete her training."

"You seem already to have made up your mind," Dr. Mowbray had said drily. "But perhaps it's not too late for a word of warning. This post you're applying for may not be as good as it seems. Before you go, you should find out all you can about the man who advertised."

At the time she'd thought, "How like a man, to distrust everything foreign!" But now, sitting in the taxi behind a grubby moustachioed driver who hadn't a word of English, and waiting for Sally to beckon her from that dim little doorway through which she had disappeared, Viola Sheppard felt rather less confident and uncomfortably near to tears.

It had been so pleasant on the ship from England. They'd made friends, had even, she felt tremulously, made a conquest or two. She had hated arriving in Barcelona this

4

morning and saying goodbye, knowing that some of the others were continuing on the cruise right through the Mediterranean to Rome and Sicily. It had been like cutting oneself off from a new, exciting home. And Barcelona, for all its fine *ramblas* and medieval city tucked away behind them, seemed so different from the lively fiesta town she had visited on her honeymoon. She didn't recall it at all. But in those days she had been young and emotional and so wholly dependent on her darling Richard; Barcelona had meant simply sunshine and bunting and music and chattering people who hadn't looked quite so Spanish in the mass as they did individually.

And now here she was in a back street of one of the poor districts, wishing she had never let Sally get out of the taxi, wishing that . . .

She drew a sharp breath of relief. Here was Sally now, hurrying from that hole in the black stone wall and swinging open the door of the taxi as if demons were after her.

"What is it, darling?" Viola asked in thin anxious tones. "Isn't it the correct address?"

Sally sank into the place beside her mother and leaned forward. "Take us back to the Rambla de las Flores," she said to the driver. "Quickly, please!"

The girl was pale and trembling a little, but she smiled at her mother. "Don't worry. We'll work out something. I'm only glad you didn't go in with me."

"But what happened?" demanded Viola, her voice rising. "You look as if you've had the most dreadful shock."

"I suppose I have." Sally's lower lip was drawn between her teeth for a moment. "There was a woman in that house — a coarse creature. She . . . she laughed at me."

"Laughed?" Viola was totally bewildered. "What did she laugh about?"

The taxi jolted out of a narrow street into a wider one, and Sally let out a sigh of complete relief. She asked, "Did you send money to that man who engaged you?"

Viola nodded. "Fifty pounds. I didn't like to tell you about it. The man wrote that it was a . . . a sort of fidelity bond and said he would return it as soon as I arrived. Didn't you see him at all?"

"He's a confidence man. The police took him away a couple of days ago."

"Oh, no!"

"I'm afraid so. He's been doing this sort of thing throughout France and Spain, but finally the police caught up with him. We haven't any hope of getting posts here, even if we could get the necessary permits. That was why the woman laughed."

"Oh, but — Sally! What are we going to do?"

They were entering one of the side streets that led down to the Rambla de las Flores, and Sally placed her hand over her mother's and nodded towards the buildings. "We're nearly there. This is horrible, but don't let's get upset about it. We can afford to stay at the hotel for a few nights while we make plans. Please don't worry. There are two of us, after all."

But Viola Sheppard's tears gently overflowed. "What a fool I am. I made you come here, Sally. You gave up St. Alun's . . ."

"You mustn't blame yourself. You're fifty pounds short, but apart from that nothing dreadful has happened. We had a lovely ten days on the ship and it's done you lots of good. At the worst, we'll have a few days in Barcelona and then do the homeward trip."

"But, darling, I can't bear the thought of going back! You don't know how much I'm depending on . . . Oh, dear, there's nothing to depend on, is there? I don't seem able to manage my life any more. When your father . . ."

"Please," whispered Sally desperately. "The taxi is stopping and you mustn't look so distressed in the street. You do have me to depend on, you know."

Viola's sweet smile shone through tears. "It's lucky you're not like me, isn't it? You're small and slim as I am, but you have a backbone and I haven't. Do you think we could get a cup of tea?"

The sudden change from despair to a plea for the commonplace was just what Sally had needed. She gave an unsteady little laugh, said, "Of course we can," and helped her mother out of the taxi. She paid the driver, and as the taxi moved away she drew a long breath and looked down the great wide thoroughfare that was thronged with people and gay with color.

It was four o'clock and Barcelona was getting into its stride after siesta. Under bright parasols stood the vendors of all kinds of flowers and fruits, of cage birds and tortoises, of kittens and goldfish and even of tiny monkeys.

Sally became aware, as she and her mother moved slowly along the pavement, that they were being extracted from the crowd like a couple of unusual specimens in a zoology class. These men who sat drinking coffee or wine and talking business, broke off to watch the passing of the neat *señora* in pale grey with lavender hair and dainty feet and the very blonde *señorita* in white and pink. The older one was beautiful, like fragile china. The young one was tanned a honey-brown, like a tourist, her hair was cut short and her eyes were a dark and velvety blue; she made one think of a soft summer night, of roses and oleanders peeping over a rough stone wall and of guitars sending out their eternal, vibrant message of love. The men thought, shrugged their regrets and went back to their wine and business.

Their glances did not register very deeply with Sally. She was frightened. Not for anything would she have described to her mother the full horror of her visit to that gloomy little hovel, but it had shaken her to the roots.

Back in England, when her mother had coaxed and argued and pleaded, Sally had felt that in pointing out the defects of the proposed move to Barcelona she was being selfish and brutal. She had been only too willing to agree that her mother needed a long holiday in a warm climate, but the idea of Viola Sheppard, the beloved and much-spoiled wife of Richard Sheppard, holding down a job in a foreign city that she had visited only once, more than twenty years ago, had seemed at the least fantastic. Then Viola had suggested that Sally wasn't interested in her mother's health, that all she cared about was her own nursing career. That had hurt, because Sally had put up with a good deal of inconvenience and long bus journeys so that her mother should not live alone in the Kensington flat. But she had understood Viola's reaction. When a woman has been lovingly cared for for twenty years and then suddenly found the love and protection withdrawn, a break-up is almost inevitable.

After the first month or two of demoralizing loneliness her mother had tried quite hard to get back into the world. For a while she had assisted in the West End beauty salon run by one of her friends, but that phase had ended when she caught 'flu and developed congestion of the lungs. She had got through all right, but the illness had run away with an enormous amount of money. Doctor and specialist, nurses, a daily servant, fresh flowers for the bedroom, fine bed-jackets and wraps and nightdresses, new bed-linen in pastel tints, new curtains and bed-cover, a new armchair in the bedroom; Sally hadn't begrudged her mother a single item that might help her to get well. But it had been alarming, afterwards, to discover how little ready money was left.

Eventually, Viola herself was forced to mention it. "Mowbray says I definitely need at least a month in a warm climate, and that I may have to spend next winter abroad. How on earth are we going to manage it, Sally? I'd have to look for a post of some sort, but what could I do? My only working experience has been the few months at the beauty salon."

"We could probably manage a month for you at one of the smaller French resorts," Sally had said. "You wouldn't have to think about anything till you got back."

"And next winter?" Viola had demanded a little querulously. "I couldn't face that horrible lung congestion again. I really couldn't."

Sally had known her mother was watching the small-ads; they had discussed one or two possibilities and discarded them. Then came the opportunity in Barcelona, and Viola had said, quite excitedly,

"It was made just for me! Running a beauty shop is all I can do, and Barcelona does happen to be a town I've toured. I'm going to write to this man, Sally. I must!"

No harm in a letter, Sally had decided. But quite soon there had been two or three letters between Mrs. Sheppard and the man in Barcelona. And in the end, because for the first time since Richard Sheppard had died her mother was alert and happy, and because she herself could see no way of paying for her mother to spend next winter in a warm climate, Sally gave in. With a bright smile and a heavy heart she had resigned from St. Alun's, booked passages on the "Bellesta" and watched her mother sign away the flat.

She had to admit that those ten days on the ship had been wonderful . . . and heartbreaking. Everyone fell in love in the moonlight on deck, of course, but Sally hadn't thought of that when Peter Malling had kissed her and told her she was beautiful.

"There aren't so many men at this café," Viola was saying plaintively. "It's awfully warm, for March, and my feet ache. I suppose it's the hard pavements after wearing sandals on deck. Shall we sit?"

They took seats at a table on the edge of the pavement café and ordered tea. Well, here we are, thought Sally bleakly. Barcelona . . . no less; the most dazzling city on the Spanish coast. And all she wanted was to get away again as fast as possible, to leave behind the bad taste of the woman in the hovel, and of failure.

"Look over there," her mother murmured eagerly. "Some of the people from the ship, and Marcus is with them. He's seen us — I'm so glad!"

But as she saw him Sally was instantly aware of that oddly awkward feeling that Marcus Durant had roused in her on board. He was something over thirty, very dark and good-looking in a rather unusual way. His features were long, his cheekbones high, but instead of the usual straight nose which is normal to such bone structure his nose was long and slightly humped at the bridge, the septum well defined. He was like a handsome hawk, and

9

Sally had no experience of hawks, handsome or otherwise. That was why she had spoken to him on the ship only when he had addressed her. He made her feel young and inadequate and even a bit laughable. And no girl of nineteen cares to feel that she has stirred only patronage and amusement in a good-looking bachelor.

But Viola had liked him immensely. "He's a real man — British with a dash of Spanish — which means that he knows how to treat a woman. He's charming and worldly and very rich!"

He was also most kind, as they had discovered on reaching Barcelona. He had escorted the two women and their luggage to the hotel and had a special word with the manager. And when he had left them he had promised to get in touch with them again from his home on the island of San Palos.

Marcus had left his companions and was approaching them with a light, enquiring smile. "Hallo there, you two. Couldn't you rest till you'd seen some of the sights?"

Viola waved one of her thin graceful hands. "Do sit down with us, Marcus. We're in such a muddle, and you're just the man to put us right."

"Please, Mother," said Sally in an undertone, and then she shut up because the man had turned his dark, questioning gaze upon her.

"Sally feels we've accepted enough help from you, and I dare say she's right," sighed Viola. "But for myself I'm overjoyed that you didn't go straight back to the ship. Marcus, what do you think has happened?" she asked dramatically.

"You've left something valuable on board?"

"Oh, no, nothing so simple as that." And Viola went ahead and told him the whole business, while Sally resolutely looked away at the passing crowds and the flowers and the traffic.

"So you see," her mother ended in soft, rueful tones, "we're more or less stranded. I feel so tired and upset that I can hardly think for myself. Sally says she'll manage everything, but I don't think she realizes even yet how much I dread going back to England. You see," with a brave smile, "I'd be so distressed that the trip home wouldn't do me any good at all, and I'd spend the whole summer wondering whether it was going to be my last."

"Mother, please . . ."

"Darling," her mother said in her clear light tones, "that's exactly how I feel about returning to England, and you know it. Marcus is well acquainted with Spain and he can advise us."

His hand covered Viola's small fist on the table and gave it a brotherly squeeze; he rested a tolerant smile upon Sally. "You're not Atlas, my child," he said. "Let me handle this. I might mention that if I'd known you two were quite friendless in Barcelona I wouldn't have left you till I'd seen you safely into someone else's hands. Your mother assured me she'd been here before and I took it for granted she had friends here. But if you've no friends and no reasons for staying, why hang on in Barcelona at all? More than half the passengers have left the ship and they won't take many new ones aboard, so you'd easily get a cabin. Why not travel on to San Palos?"

Sally widened her violet-blue eyes. "San Palos! We're not plutocrats, Mr. Durant."

"You're being rude," said her mother in shaky, reproving tones. "At least give Marcus time to finish what he was proposing for us."

He smiled. "Thank you," he said, with a mockingly polite inclination of his head towards Sally. "I've told you about San Palos. It's just a small island, about ten miles by four, and three-quarters of it is covered by vineyards and perfume farms."

"All of which are yours," said Viola, in comforted tones. "That Spanish grandmother of yours must have been a remarkable woman."

"She still is. Eighty-seven, forced to be physically inactive, but full of fight. Well, the last quarter of the island is a portion that's spread round a very fine natural harbor which has been leased to the Royal Navy. I believe they do testing, chiefly, and it's not a very important station,

11

but there's quite a number of personnel living in a block of flats and fifty or sixty houses, and I'm sure the wives would be only too happy to patronize an English beauty expert."

"Oh, but I'm no expert! I suppose almost any woman knows how a beauty salon is run simply by going there regularly for her own requirements, but I couldn't actually *do* very much."

"We'd have to look into it for you, but I've no doubt something could be fixed up. And your daughter . . ." He looked at her again, speculatively. "You're a nurse, aren't you?"

"Second year."

He considered this. "There's no general hospital on San Palos, but we do have a nursing home which has been enlarged recently. They added a small block to deal with the cases from Naval Town and they might be able to use you there. It wouldn't count as training, perhaps, but then neither would any post you might have managed to get here in Barcelona."

Sally wished she didn't feel so awkward with this man. Usually she got along very well with men, but Marcus Durant gave her the queer conviction that he was slicing the ground from under her feet.

"I can't be sure the nursing home will take me on; I can't speak Spanish, anyway. In the vicinity of Barcelona there's a large English-speaking colony . . ."

"In San Palos, too," he said smoothly. "Not quite so large, but it's there. As it happens, my cousin is the doctor-in-charge at the nursing home, and I'm sure I could persuade him to use you in the new block, where the patients are chiefly from the English families at Naval Town. Until you were settled in a place of your own, I should be most happy to have you both stay at Las Viñas as my guests."

"Well, how very generous of you, Marcus," exclaimed Viola, gratefully. "Sally, isn't that splendid?"

But Sally was still feeling desperate. "One can't make a sudden decision on a matter of this kind . . ."

"I'm afraid you'll have to," Marcus broke in calmly. "The ship is due to sail in about two hours. That gives us time to visit the shipping office and book a cabin for two more nights. Did you unpack?"

"No." Viola was smiling almost happily. "We slipped a couple of frocks from one case, that's all. Marcus, you don't know how I feel about this."

"We mustn't waste time," he said. "We'll get a taxi and drop Sally off at the hotel. She can pack the few things you've left about and have the porter bring the luggage into the foyer. You and I will do the booking — you do have your passports with you?"

"Sally looks after them; I'm really not to be trusted with important documents. And I think it would be better the other way round, Marcus. I'll go to the hotel and wait for you, and Sally will go with you to the shipping office. She knows more about these things than I do."

"Good." He was standing. "Have you finished your tea?"

He called the waiter and paid, hailed a taxi and put them both inside, but himself took the seat next to the driver. Within five minutes he was taking Viola into the hotel, and a minute later he was seated beside Sally and the taxi was moving down towards the Plaza de San Jaime.

He looked at Sally's tender, charming little face, solemn now with anxiety. "If I hadn't met you and your mother you'd have reason to look depressed," he said with a touch of impatience. "It makes me shiver to think of you two adrift in a foreign city. Innocents abroad, if I ever saw a couple!"

"We'd have managed something," she said stiffly. "You mustn't think I don't appreciate all you're doing for us, but I can't help feeling uncertain."

"I'm doing nothing that any other man wouldn't do. As a matter of fact I'm saving myself a journey back to Barcelona. Your mother promised to write to me at San Palos and tell me how you were getting along. If I'd heard about this disappointment of yours I'd certainly have come here for you."

She looked fleetingly at his lean profile. "But why? The few days aboard the 'Bellesta' don't make you responsible for our mistakes. We don't really know you at all well."

"*You* don't know me, because you were having fun with the younger set. I had a good many conversations with your mother, though, and learned all about her problems." He smiled. "She let me down at the bridge table, and when I sponsored her in the tape-cutting Derby she came last. But I didn't hold it against her. She's a very sweet person."

"I still think it's peculiar that you should want to do so much for us. Don't think I'm ungrateful. I just don't understand."

He shrugged. "You're very young, and I hope you'll forgive me for mentioning that you're still quivering from the affair with the pianist chap who left the ship at Malaga." Reasoningly he added, "He wasn't so very good, you know. When he gave the concert I thought his Chopin a trifle ragged in parts, and he really hasn't the gusto for Beethoven. I almost went to sleep."

"You're probably not in the least musical," she said distantly. "An impresario thought Peter good enough for a tour through Spain."

He nodded understandingly. "Good enough for some of the minor cities, perhaps. He'll have to put in a lot of work before he'll make Madrid, though. However, he's only about twenty-five, so there's plenty of time for his playing to mature, emotionally. You knew him for only a week; it wasn't long enough to start anything that might go deep."

"I don't think you know much about feelings, Mr. Durant."

"I shan't call you Miss Sheppard, so you'd better make it Marcus. Feelings? They're overrated and overworked. One should never marry because of feelings; they're as fickle as a beautiful woman." And without pause: "Here's the shipping office. As you're an alien you'll have to go in with me."

"Aren't you an alien?"

14

"Not exactly. My grandmother's family is very old and well known, and its name happens to be my middle name — del Moscado. These people handle a good deal of shipping for us."

It was obvious the moment they entered the office of the shipping company that to the officials there Mr. Durant was a personage. He got exactly what he asked for and was told it was no trouble at all; the account would come through in the usual way. Being Spaniards, the clerks took great interest in Marcus's young companion, and when eventually Sally found herself back in the taxi she realized that her cheeks were hot and she didn't want to look at the man. Marcus seemed to have noticed nothing.

"Now we'll pick up your mother and drive to the harbor," he said. "Easy wasn't it?"

"Yes."

"Aren't you relieved?"

"Naturally."

"But you feel you're exchanging one queer situation for another? Let me assure you that San Palos is a friendly island; you'll probably be far happier there than you could ever have been in Barcelona." On a note of finality, he ended, "This arrangement we've made is best for both you and your mother, believe me."

But Sally couldn't leave it there. "I still feel you're doing too much for us, and that at least you should let us stay at an hotel on San Palos."

He lifted his shoulders in a faintly foreign way. "It could be arranged, but as you feel I am today doing you a favor, you may not object if I ask in return the favor of your spending at least a few days at Las Viñas. We can talk it over later. Just now it's more important to get back on board and settle into your new cabin."

*   *   *

As the "Bellesta" steamed on through the Mediterranean that night Viola, in a silk wrap and toeless mules, stood creaming her face and looking through the porthole at the wine-dark sky spattered with stars.

"Isn't it heavenly?" she said, with a dreamy expression in her light blue eyes. "To think that tonight we might have been tossing about in hotel beds and wondering how on earth we'd handle the situation! But here we are, back on this lovely ship for two more days, with San Palos to look forward to at the end. We're very fortunate, Sally. Marcus may be a wee bit cynical in his outlook, but he's most dependable. So lucky that he happens to like us!"

"It's you he likes."

"You too, darling. I remember his saying during the trip that you're pretty and gentle and yet spirited." She laughed a little. "Remember the night of the ball, when he danced with you? He told me that the moment the dance ended you bucked off like a frightened deer."

"I suppose he thought that very funny — and it's not even true." Sally climbed on to her bed and sat there, cross-legged. "I can't help it if he makes me feel he's taking the mickey all the time. He's too darned superior."

"Well, he's not a medical student or a budding pianist," Viola pointed out. "Marcus is thirty-two, and he's been in sole command of Las Viñas since he was twenty. He spends a lot of time in England, but mostly he lives on the island, in the mansion built by his great-grandfather, or perhaps it's even great-great; I'm not sure. You can't expect him to be just an ordinary Englishman."

"I'd sooner deal with an ordinary Englishman any time," stated Sally firmly. "At least you can take a good guess at what they're thinking. Marcus Durant has a personal reason for everything he does — I'm sure of it."

"That's very unfair, dear," said Viola, clamping a lid on to her cream jar. "The truth of it is that we looked rather appealingly small and scared and he instantly felt protective. And frankly, that's how I like a man to be. He'll do everything he can to get us established on San Palos, and for a whole year we needn't even think of the future." Her voice quivered slightly. "You can't imagine what a tremendous relief that is to me."

16

Instantly Sally was all contrition. "But I can, of course I can! There's nothing I want more than to have you thoroughly happy in a warm climate. That's why we gave up everything in England." Impulsively, she slipped down to the rug once more and hugged her mother. "I don't really mind Marcus Durant. He's rich and arrogant and he tells fibs. I wasn't afraid of him when we danced, only uneasy! — but I'm as grateful as you are that he's helping us. I think you may be happier on San Palos than you would have been in Barcelona; life won't be so demanding."

But after Viola had slipped into bed and put out her light, Sally lay thinking. First of all, very deliberately, about Peter Malling. She saw Peter's lock of lank hair over his deep brow, his soft hazel eyes and the pale, almost fluid fingers. Dancing with him had been like drifting to music through clouds; and they'd had such lovely talks. And in the mornings, while stewards were still putting the big main lounge to rights, they had stolen through to the Bechstein, and he'd played, just for Sally.

Suddenly, jarringly, she recalled one morning, just before they had reached Malaga. She had been half lying in a chair, listening to a nocturne with her eyes closed. The music had ended and she'd stirred, and opened her eyes to observe through a window the experienced, half derisive smile of Marcus Durant. He'd no doubt been striding round the deck before breakfast, heard the music and halted to listen. His shoulders had looked big in the white shirt, and the blue scarf about his throat had somehow emphasized that hawklike look of his. He'd given her half a wink and moved on, and Sally remembered reflecting that the man definitely had a past, and possibly a present, if one knew all!

To her mother, of course, he was just an experienced, interesting man who would help them. The fact that his family owned most of San Palos rather brightened his aura, but that was all. Naïvely, she simply thought they had been wonderfully lucky, that in Marcus Durant's hands their immediate future was secure.

And no doubt it was, Sally sighed to herself. It wasn't that she couldn't accept benefits when they were offered in the right spirit; the man was just a bit overwhelming in his generosity, that was all. This cabin, for instance. Their earlier one had been on the inside, without a port-hole; it had had two bunks, one above the other, instead of beds, and there had been hardly room to move between the dressing chest and the wardrobe cupboard. This cabin was one of the spacious outside ones, of which there were only half a dozen in the ship; its cost was nearly double that of the inside accommodation. Marcus had a whole cabin to himself, next door but one. When her mother had exclaimed delightedly, and then demurred, the beastly man had said, "The cost was exactly the same as for an inside cabin. I'll show you the voucher, if you like." Which meant they were travelling as protégées of Marcus del Moscado Durant!

The swish of the ocean beyond the porthole was soothing, and soon Sally forgot her uncertainties and slipped into a doze; to be awakened by the sudden flowering of the light over her mother's bed. Viola was sitting up, searching frantically in her handbag.

"I'm too wound up to sleep," she wailed. "I decided to swallow a capsule in the dark and then I remembered they're in the case where we locked our money. I was hoping I'd find a loose capsule here in my bag, but there isn't one."

"Of course there isn't," said Sally drowsily. "Give me the key and I'll get them for you. Where is the key, by the way?"

"Don't you remember? We had dinner in here and then went above for some air. You had the keys in your hand when we met Marcus. You dropped them and he picked them up and put them into his pocket. I distinctly recollect his saying you mustn't forget to ask for them. Oh, dear, and I'm starting a headache. I must have a capsule or I'll be fit for nothing tomorrow."

"Don't panic. Are you sure an aspirin wouldn't do the trick?"

"Darling, you know me," said her mother dolefully. "Once I decide I'm not going to sleep, I just stay awake feeling more and more wretched as the night passes. And aspirin always make me shiver — you know that. If you'd let me keep the capsules in my bag . . ." She let it tail off.

"Perhaps if you swallow an aspirin and I massage your neck?" Sally sugested. "It's helped before."

"But we weren't on a ship. Darling, please go and get the keys from Marcus!"

"I can't do that — it's so late."

"Only eleven-thirty. If you don't want to go to Marcus, try the doctor."

"Yes, I'll do that. Lie down again. I'll be as quick as I can."

Sally pulled on her flowered cotton wrap and tied the girdle, ran fingers through her short pale hair, blinked herself more wide awake and opened the cabin door. The wide corridor shone dully in the small night illumination; light blue rubberized flooring with a black border. She stepped out, wondered whether she should first find the night stewardess, and took a few paces along the corridor. Then she halted. How did ships' doctors react to being wakened up in order to supply a sleeping pill for someone else? Sally had a healthy respect for doctors of all kinds, and from her own experience she was pretty sure that the "Bellesta's" doctor was as averse to being roused for trifles as others she'd known. On a ship, there were probably a good many sleepless people, but they didn't all plague the doctor for relief — not late at night, anyway. Her mother's case was a little different, though. The nervous collapse last year, after her husband's death, her illness and the long months of lassitude and weakness . . . surely the doctor wouldn't mind the small inconvenience, just this once?

Sally moved on, and stopped again, precipitately. Marcus had come into sight at the end of the corridor. He was still in a dinner jacket, and had probably been playing cards with some of the other men. Her fingers pulled the lapels of her wrap together, and as he reached her she smiled at him, a little weakly.

"What's the matter?" he asked at once. "Your mother unwell?"

"No. She can't sleep, that's all. You took care of our keys — do you mind letting me have them back?"

"They're in my cabin. I brought them down about an hour ago, but your light was out, so I slipped them into a drawer. I'll get them for you."

They were only a pace or two from his door. He opened it and left it wide. Sally moved into the doorway and leaned there, looking young and sleepy. He had the keys and was tossing them in his hand.

"What have the keys to do with your mother's insomnia?" he asked.

"We keep certain things locked up in one of our cases. I always take charge of the keys and the sleeping pills."

He sounded a trifle acid as he said, "You need to be taken care of yourself. I still shudder when I think of you two alone in Barcelona."

She smiled dimly. "I could shudder myself, but not for my own sake. My mother has always been so dependent, and I'm a very poor substitute for my father. I'm afraid she regards you as a newly acquired brother."

"That makes me your uncle, doesn't it?" he said negligently.

"You're not quite old enough — or comfortable enough."

"Thanks for the compliment, even though you didn't mean it that way." He paused, a small smile on his lips. "You're glad I got you out of Barcelona, but you still dislike me, don't you?"

"I just don't understand you," she said quickly. "You're kind but . . . but cold, and I'm not used to dealing with someone who seems to . . . to sneer at any woman who's younger than himself."

He didn't deny it, but the sarcastic smile became set. He held out the keys and she took them. And then, from close by in the corridor, came the sound of unmusical humming, and a fattish man of about forty lurched into view. He was wearing a voluminous red dressing gown and a monocle through which he peered short-sightedly into the cabin.

"Marcus, ol' boy!" he growled jovially. "I knew you were aboard, but . . ." He became aware of Sally and bowed exaggeratedly. "The little woman, eh? Honeymoon and all that? How de do, my dear. I'm Jim McCartney. Isn't that right, Marcus? Jim McCartney?"

Involuntarily, Marcus had put his arm about Sally's shoulders and drawn her a short way into the cabin and away from the swaying man in the doorway.

"Yes, that's right," he said. "How are you, Jim?"

"Fine . . . fine. Spent the evening in my cabin with an old pal. Had two days in Barcelona, but got to get back." He went owlishly serious. "You've heard about your dear old Doña Inez? It was a bad attack, ol' boy; by all accounts the next one will be her last."

The fingers on Sally's shoulders tightened excruciatingly. He doesn't even know what he's gripping, she thought faintly, and bore the agony without a murmur.

"My grandmother has had a heart attack?" Marcus said swiftly. "When was it?"

"About a week ago. A sort of stroke, I think." The man gave a falsely hearty laugh. "She's a great woman, though. She intended to stay alive and see you married. And she's done it, eh? You haven't introduced me to the wife, Marcus."

Marcus' hands dropped suddenly to his sides. "I'm not married," he said abruptly. "This is Miss Sheppard."

The other's bleary eyes focused with difficulty upon Sally's tousled fair hair and her slim shoulders in the wrap. "Only engaged? Well, perhaps that's better still. Ol' lady always wanted you to marry on San Palos, didn't she? Pretty girl you've picked, Marcus. But then trust you."

"I suggest you go back to your cabin, Jim. I'll see you tomorrow."

The man wagged a roguish finger. "Did I interrupt something? You were saying goodnight and ol' Jim crashed in. Sorry . . . sorry . . ."

He still murmured the word at intervals as he weaved a path through his own private haze towards the other end of the corridor. Marcus drew a sharp breath.

"The man runs an hotel in Naval Town," he said. "He's good-hearted, but a soak and a gossip."

Her throat a little dry, Sally asked, "Did he know what he was saying?"

"Partly, but don't worry. By the time he sobers up in San Palos he'll have forgotten he came to this cabin tonight."

"He hadn't forgotten about your grandmother. I'm terribly sorry to hear she's so ill. Isn't it odd, that they didn't cable you?"

"They probably cabled me in London. I'm returning earlier than they expected and I generally travel by air." With a preoccupied frown he added, "Doña Inez is very old and she's become fiercely set in her ideas — at least, she had. I'm all she has." He gestured briefly, and went with her to the door of the cabin she shared with her mother. "This isn't your affair. I'm sorry you were dragged into it. Goodnight."

His offhandedness hurt like the dully shattering impact of a club. Sally answered him and slipped into the cabin.

Her mother said plaintively, "You were such a long time, darling. Did you have to fight with that doctor?"

She didn't seem to require an answer, or to be surprised that Sally had the keys. She swallowed her capsule, lay down tidily and closed her eyes. But Sally, after the light was out, lay staring into the darkness. She didn't know why, but she felt quite sick and despondent.

The next day passed quickly. The ship put into Marseilles, and Sally spent the day touring the port with a group of young people; she also sat with them through the film show in the ship's lounge that evening, while her mother chatted gaily on deck with the captain and others.

To Sally's relief, both Marcus and the affably cock-eyed Jim McCartney were missing.

The ship anchored off San Palos in brilliant sunshine at nine-thirty next morning. To the left, Sally could see the curve of Naval Bay with its line of new concrete buildings, its old town and the official airstrip. To the right, the island was green and hilly, with small pastel-tinted houses dropped here and there like toys. There was an old straggling village adjoining Navay Town, and a waterfront that looked as though it were a piece of washed cliffside, it was so pink and rough.

Passengers who were continuing on the voyage swarmed ashore for their ration of sightseeing. Sally had packed early, but Viola would never be rushed. It was not till Marcus came to hurry them that she finally said she was ready. When she came out on deck she made suitable exclamations. What a dream of an island! And that was Naval Bay? And what were the trees in that orchard on the hillside — olives and figs and almonds? Warmed by the Mediterranean sun and a new sense of security, Viola was prepared to love everything.

There were no customs formalities. A swarthy porter in a peaked cap loaded the trunk and bags on to a trolley and trundled away towards an ancient converted bus which was apparently the freight car of San Palos.

Marcus led the way to the taxi he had ordered, and made Viola comfortable in the back seat. He was about to do the same with Sally when a dusty grey car drew up a few yards ahead of them and a slim man in a light suit got out of it and came back, to meet them with an outstretched hand.

"Well, Carlos!" said Marcus. "How did you know I was on the 'Bellesta'?"

But Carlos, who looked about forty and was a polite Spaniard, bowed towards Sally. First things first, his attitude said.

"Sally, this is my cousin, Carlos Suarez. He's the doctor who'll find something for you to do at the nursing home. Carlos . . . meet Sally Sheppard. Mrs. Sheppard is already in the taxi."

During the next few moments, Carlos bowed almost inside the taxi and Viola accepted the fact that he was charmed to meet her. He bent over Sally's hand with a smile that said she was attractive and he approved of her.

Then he answered Marcus's question. "I was just leaving the house of a patient back there when I saw McCartney of the hotel. He told me you were on the ship, and I may say I was never more glad to hear such news."

"How is Doña Inez?" came the quick demand.

A Latin shrug. "She lives. That great-aunt of mine is the most determined woman of eighty-seven I have ever known. She is waiting only for your return — with Miss Sheppard."

A chill crept over Sally's skin. She said, "I think Mr. McCartney must have . . ."

But Marcus cut her off smoothly. "We're going up to Las Viñas at once, Carlos. As Doña Inez doesn't know I'm coming, perhaps you and I had better see her together."

"I am so sorry, but I have an operation in half an hour. But do not fear for Doña Inez. She will not die of seeing you, Marcus. She was hoping you would bring home a bride, but a fiancée will do almost as well. In fact," with a humorous lift of the shoulders, "it will give her a new lease of life. She will be more determined than ever to see you married."

"You don't understand," said Sally in breathless tones. "You see . . ."

"Carlos has to leave us," Marcus said coolly. And turning to his cousin, "I should like to know exactly what we may expect with Doña Inez. Perhaps you will come to Las Viñas for dinner tonight?"

"Thank you, Marcus. I shall be delighted." The doctor made his bows. He said, "I wish you great happiness here on San Palos, señorita, and it is most pleasing that you are interested in our little hospital. Perhaps," with a very kind smile, "you are rather younger than we all imagined, but that is no drawback. I am only surprised that Marcus was able to leave you in England after your engagement last year; in his place, I would have insisted on bringing you

24

home, even then!" A click of the heels, a smiling *"Adios!"* and the doctor returned to his car.

Firm fingers on her arm were guiding Sally round to the other side of the taxi. Dazedly she tried to stop, but Marcus said quietly,

"Temporarily, it seems, we're engaged. Say nothing at all to your mother. We'll talk later."

Then Sally was subsiding into squashy old leather and feeling quite boneless and wooly-headed. She turned and met her mother's smiling glance.

"What were you talking about out there — a job at the nursing home?"

"No," Sally managed. "It's too soon for that."

"Never mind. We won't think about work for a few days — just wallow in idleness and luxury at Las Viñas."

Very clearly, Sally said, "I'm not sure we should go to Las Viñas. We might be in the way."

Marcus turned round from his seat beside the driver. "You will certainly stay at Las Viñas," he said flatly, sounding rather foreign. "We have many rooms and the staff to look after them. It is settled."

Settled, thought Sally dazedly. Settled? That cousin of his, the doctor, actually thought that Marcus Durant was engaged to Sally Sheppard! Anything more fantastic it would be hard to concoct, and yet Marcus had let the man go on believing it. Marcus, it seemed, had become engaged last year to someone in England; she should have been on the "Bellesta" with him, but for some reason she had stayed behind. People were mistaking Sally for that woman, and Marcus was . . . was letting them.

The whole thing was incredible and infuriating, and typically, Marcus had masterfully told her to keep quiet about it. Did he think she was a dummy, or something? Did he think . . .

think . . .

Sally's teeth were so tightly clenched that they hurt, and she was angry in a way she had never known before. It was frightening.

CHAPTER TWO

LAS VINAS had been built in spacious days. Pure Spanish in style, its cloistered whiteness spread in a curve round a magnificent paved courtyard where a central pool covered with lilies was only a gracious detail. Palms shaded one side of the courtyard, and here an ornate wrought-iron table and padded chairs were set, and a very old Sealyham snoozed in their shade.

When Sally, having unpacked in a white and blue bedroom for her mother and in a white and lilac bedroom for herself, came outdoors in a desperate attempt to get back to reality, she found an old servant laying the luncheon table. The woman wore black with a white apron, and she gave an old-fashioned curtsey which made Sally feel a bigger fraud than ever. The situation was impossible.

She went to the low wall and looked down past a rockery at a sweep of bright flower beds and shrubberies. The cypresses beyond marked the limit of the private garden, and behind them was the white wall that confined it. From here it was impossible to see the tall ornamental gates in the arched entrance to Las Viñas, but Sally remembered her own feelings as the taxi had passed under the arch. A rush of panic, chiefly, but also a foolishly hopeless regret that they had met Marcus Durant after that appalling visit in Barcelona. Then, she had felt she hardly knew Marcus; now, she was fatalistically certain that only unhappiness could come from knowing him.

Oh, dear, and this was such a lovely place. One could be tremendously happy just living in this atmosphere and rambling over the hills and down to the beaches. The miles of vineyards had looked a sparkling green, the people were wholesome and rugged, and there was a British contingent down at Naval Bay, so that one needn't even feel homesick. And if she could have worked at the nursing home while her mother had some light job in the town, Sally would never have dreamed of asking more from life. It would have been the fullest, happiest existence any girl could wish for. She sighed.

Just behind her a thick feminine voice said, "You will pardon me, *señorita*. Señor Durant has asked me to introduce myself. I am Katarina, the companion of Doña Inez."

Sally turned, and met a pair of enigmatic dark eyes. The woman was pale yellow and sharp-featured, with a mole that sprouted three belligerent hairs near the left corner of her brown-lipped mouth. Her hair, black with streaks of grey, was drawn back smoothly into a knot, and she wore the usual black frock, though it was a little more dressy than the servants' thick cotton; an oldish matt silk with a high neck, blouse-effect top and straight skirt. Sally was irresistibly reminded of Victorian illustrations, but before she could smile Katarina's heavy eyelids flicked down over her eyes, and the effect was disturbing.

"I'm glad to know you, Katarina," Sally said politely. "How is Doña Inez?"

"She sleeps much of the time. I do not think she will awaken before evening, but it will be a joyful awakening, no? There is no one in the world she loves so well as Don Marcus."

The prefix to his name made him a foreigner, and caused Sally an inward shiver. "I do hope my mother and I won't cause too much extra work in the house," she murmured, for something to say.

"But where else would you stay? This will be your home, and also that of Señora Sheppard. This is a great day for Las Viñas."

She didn't sound thrilled, but why should she? thought Sally despairingly. How much did she know? And how much had already been said between this woman and Marcus? If only he'd come out, so that she could tell him she had no intention of staying in this place under false pretences!

"You're very kind," she said automatically. "I'm a nurse, you know. If there's anything I can do to help you, please let me know."

27

The woman drew back and clasped her hands in front of her. In stilted tones she answered, "I am very capable of taking care of Doña Inez. A young nurse would be quite out of place in the bedroom of the *señora*. You will excuse me, please?"

Oh, heavens. A clanger, if ever there was one; and she'd probably go on making them because she was not only angry but nervous. Sally conjured a smile as Katarina went into the house, and turned back to sigh once more at the garden. But in a moment her mother came out, looking small and radiant in delphinium blue. She came beside Sally, threw out both hands at the view.

"Isn't it splendid? I'm sure it's the healthiest spot on earth!"

"They have a large nursing home," Sally reminded her drily.

"Bound to be a few accidents, and babies," came the airy rejoinder. "I can't imagine any place lovelier than this. And isn't the house beautiful? All that carved oak and lovely porcelain, and the light restful bedrooms. Have you seen Marcus since we arrived?"

"No."

"Don't snap, darling. The trouble with young people is that they haven't yet learned how to accept things gracefully. We're not here just accidentally, you know. Even before we reached Barcelona Marcus said we must visit him here some time. He even made me promise to write and tell him how we were getting on."

"Yes, I know."

"Then please, Sally, try to look as though you are enjoying yourself. Here we are, with servants simply falling over themselves to do things for us, in a dream of a house on a dazzling green island, and it does seem that you should be grateful enough to smile about it. I do *need* it, you know, dear."

"Yes. I'm sorry. I suppose I still feel we should have stayed at the hotel." She changed the topic. "Have you ever seen rock plants like those down there? The miniature cacti are amusing, aren't they?"

Talk of the garden occupied them till the lunch trolley and Marcus appeared simultaneously. He seated the two women at the table, smiled and apologized for having looked through his mail before lunch.

"I do have a man who comes in to do secretarial work for me two or three days a week, but he doesn't yet know that I'm back. Fortunately, there's nothing that can't wait till tomorrow. Cold consommé, Viola, or would you prefer hors d'oeuvres?"

It was a good lunch, the early fruits were delicious and the coffee excellent. But Sally was too inwardly restless to eat cheerfully, and by the time Marcus was sitting back and suavely offering cigarettes she was so knotted up that she could have screamed. Perhaps Marcus sensed her taut-ness, for as soon as they had finished coffee he said.

"You'll find the *siesta* is a good habit, Viola. An hour's sleep after lunch makes you feel good for the rest of the day. Do you like your room?"

"Enormously. And since leaving England I've acquired the habit of an afternoon rest, and can't do without it." She looked up at him as he stood with her. "Sally's a wee bit blue, Marcus. I don't think she's been quite so bright since we lost that delightful young pianist at Malaga. Can you think of some nice man who'll cheer her up?"

"I might," he said easily, as he went with her to the nearest door into the house.

Sally had stood up too, and had moved along the court-yard towards the steps. But she hadn't quite reached them when Marcus came beside her, and they descended side by side without speaking, curved down, round the end of the rockery and on to the path below it. There, in the shade of an old magnolia tree, Sally stopped and faced him. But it was Marcus who spoke first, very calmly.

"It's not the end of the world, you know, so let's be sane about it, shall we?"

"I'll try, but it's not going to be easy. I know you're someone rather marvellous here on San Palos, but I'm just not the type to be overawed into posing as something I'm not. I think I have a right to demand that you make it quite clear to everyone that my mother and I are merely two people you took pity on in Barcelona!"

With dangerous softness he answered, "I'm hardly likely to make that kind of statement about my house guests; even you know enough about me to realize that. And now, perhaps, you'll let me explain a few things. Come over here and sit down."

He motioned towards a white seat under a huge old peach tree that was a billow of pale pink blossom. They sat, Sally ramrod-straight at one end of the bench and Marcus half facing her at the other.

"Cigarette?"

"No, thank you."

He shrugged, and pushed the thin silver case back into his pocket. "All this, of course, began with McCartney's surprising us at the door of my cabin the night before last," he said evenly. "He blundered to conclusions which he's no doubt been airing down at the hotel all morning."

"You could have stopped him," she said accusingly.

"I thought I had, but the man is like a waggish bull; once he has hold of one idea there's not much room for anything else. After you'd left the cabin that night I was disturbed about it and went straight along to see him. I told him you and your mother were friends I'd met on board, but all he did was laugh and say he quite understood. I decided to leave it till yesterday, when the fumes should have dispersed."

"What happened?"

"Something I couldn't have foreseen. We'd no sooner tied up at Marseilles than the 'Bellesta,' as usual, was connected to a telephone line. McCartney's wife was in some sort of dilemma here and she phoned him to ask what she should do about it."

"Is that all?"

"It was all I found out, but it was enough. Knowing McCartney, I was pretty sure he'd tell his wife to guess who was on board . . . and all the rest of it."

"But you had no proof. Did you see the man again?"

"No, I left things alone; the more I'd said the more he was likely to make of it in the hotel saloon. Compared with my concern about Doña Inez. McCartney and his drunken rambling didn't seem very important . . . till I heard he'd been in communication with his wife." He paused. "San Palos is very beautiful, but it's small and thickly populated, and I doubt if there's a single person here who doesn't know me."

"Even so," she said, looking down at her hands, "you could have explained everything the moment we arrived. You even let your cousin the doctor think the worst."

He spoke cynically. "Is the situation so utterly distasteful? You now have quite a high position in the small world of San Palos. Doesn't that recompense you a little for the abomination of your name being linked with that of Marcus del Moscado Durant?"

She looked at him briefly. "I suppose you hate it as much as I do, but you happen to be the dictator in this. It can't possibly go on."

"Not for long." His long lean fingers drummed for a second on the back of the bench. "You're a sensitive girl, Sally, and though you confess that you find me baffling, I'm sure you understand the situation here. Let me fill in a few details. A moment ago you spoke accusingly about my allowing Carlos Suarez to believe what you termed the worst. Let me assure you at once that Carlos is an understanding type; we can take him into our confidence whenever we like. I said as little as possible to Carlos because I first wanted to get some idea of how things were here at Las Viñas."

"And . . . how are they?"

"Complicated. The gossip from the hotel got through to the servants here late last night, but Katarina waited till this morning before she told Doña Inez."

"She told her? What sort of nurse is she?"

"Katarina has been my grandmother's companion for twenty years, and before that she was her maid. She told me she broke the news very gently. First, feeling her way, she said I'd be home today. Doña Inez was happy about it, but after a few minutes she began to get a little upset." Marcus looked at the troubled face that was half turned from him. "I know you're awfully young for this, but you must try to understand."

"I'm listening," she said quietly.

"Well, it seems that Doña Inez had been sure I'd bring home a wife, but she was now afraid I'd be returning alone. She began to get so worked up that Katrina told her the rest — that I was bringing a fiancée and the fiancée's mother. After that it was all joy and excitement, and eventually Katarina gave her a sedative — from which she hasn't yet roused."

Sally drew in a dry lip, rubbed fingers along her jaw in a youthful gesture. "But you can't go on deceiving her. It's not even fair to her."

He sat straighter and said coldly, "Doña Inez is very old, and she's the person I've always cared for most. She's had a long and rather beautiful life, and I want the end of it to be in keeping. What she believes is not very important compared with the effect it will achieve." He let a moment pass before saying distinctly, "She'll want to see you — probably this evening."

Her head rose quickly and she gave him a wide alarmed stare. "Are you asking me to go on being your bogus fiancée? I won't do it!"

"Not for an old and ailing woman who believes in happy endings?"

"I'm under no obligation to your grandmother." But her voice shook. "You're quite objective about this, aren't you? Maybe you love Doña Inez, but your feelings for the rest of the sex are on the icy side. You'll have to find someone else to act the part. I couldn't go through with it."

"I think you could, quite charmingly. You're a little shy, and people will therefore be careful what they say to you. There won't be many awkward moments, and in any case I'll be right there to help you through them."

"And what about my mother?" she asked shakily. "So far, she hasn't an inkling about this ridiculous situation. She accepts the V.I.P. treatment because . . ."

"That's enough," he said curtly. "You and your mother would have had the same welcome if you'd come as ordinary guests. When I first invited you here I had no notion that Doña Inez had had the attack last week. I left her six weeks ago in good health — she didn't get up for more than a couple of hours each day, but for her age she was in good trim. Now circumstances are altered. A sharp disappointment might cause another attack — who knows?" He waited, but Sally said nothing, so he added in level tones, "Your mother would have to believe the engagement genuine."

Sally got nervously to her feet. "You expect a good deal in return for the favor in Barcelona, don't you? Even if I were willing to deceive my mother, she wouldn't believe in an engagement between us."

He pushed up from his seat and looked at her, quizzically. "You don't know Viola very well. She was young in the flapper age and she hasn't grown out of it. She's a little feather-brained, naïve and very dependent, and I'm sure that deep down she still believes in fairies. She collapsed after your father's death because she's never quite accepted the unpalatable realities of life, and after a while, inevitably, she came to lean on you instead. She doesn't find it at all difficult to believe in the things that keep life smooth and pleasant. That's why she was so keen to come to San Palos from the first moment I mentioned it."

"You think she'd regard this . . . this phoney engagement that way?"

"I'm pretty sure of it. She'll think, "How nice — he's a wee bit old for my Sally, but quite a catch." And without any mercenary intentions she'll congratulate herself on having got to know me so well on the ship that she'll now have an assured home in a good climate. I like Viola — she amuses me and rouses the protective instinct — but you have to admit she's not deep. You must take after your father."

He had got Viola off fairly pat, and as well as one or two other things, it irritated Sally. She began to walk along the path, hoping he would let her go, but he strode lazily at her side without attempting to continue the conversation. She felt him flick something from her hair — a peach-flower petal, perhaps — and the action somehow tightened the little spring that seemed coiled in her chest. There was plenty of sun-warmed air, but she found it difficult to breathe.

They were quite some way from the house, among scented shrubs and cypress trees, when she said huskily, "It all comes back to Doña Inez, doesn't it? Some time you'll have to tell her the truth."

"Carlos will decide when, but I'd say she should be strong enough to bear it about a month from the attack."

"That's three weeks from now. And my mother? You know so much about her that no doubt you can tell me exactly how she'll react to losing the good match as a son-in-law!"

"Why don't you relax?" he said mildly. "This thing might almost be fun if you'd get the right slant on it. Before we end the engagement I'll have Viola established in some business down in Naval Town. She'll be regretful but understanding. Take my word for it."

"And she'll never know she's been paid for my part in the deception!"

He stopped and made her face him. "I won't have that attitude," he said roughly. "I had every intention of setting up Viola in some sort of business before this other thing was even in the air, and you know it. It seems to me that you're letting your fright run away with you. The details of this affair can remain a secret between you and me. We'll admit Carlos if we have to, but that's all. Get one thing straight — *you'll* emerge the victor, I won't."

"What does that mean?"

"Just this. The fact of the engagement naturally implies a proposal of marriage from me to you, but its termination will show that you've turned me down." His teeth snapped. "Believe me, that's not a situation I care for very much!"

Sally suddenly knew why and it made her angry again. He really had gone to England to marry a fiancée; she knew no more than that, but it was enough.

She said slowly, "If we'd both tried to convince the McCartney man the other night this need never have happened."

"Convince him of what?" asked Marcus distinctly. "That you weren't just emerging from my cabin looking sleepy and tousled and wearing a dressing gown?"

Sally went white, her eyes were huge. "Is that . . . did he . . . ?"

"I don't know what he thought, and if you'll agree to this arrangement I won't care, either. As gossip, the item becomes rather a damp squib if we're supposed to be on the verge of getting married."

She shook her head despondently. "All this has built up so quickly that I'm far too muddled to work it out. I don't seem to have any option but to do as you ask."

"No, I don't think you have, so we'll consider it settled, shall we? And seeing that our hearts are likely to remain more or less intact, we'll go into it blithely and try to get a private kick out of it."

"I'm afraid I'm not that kind."

His glance was keen, but he said mockingly, "I'll make a bargain with you. When we agree to break off the engagement I'll give you whatever you want most. Got any ideas?"

She said dispiritedly, "All I've ever wanted is to be a good nurse . . . and perhaps to marry when I'm about twenty-five."

"They're both attainable. On the day we part company as fiancés I'll introduce you to every eligible young man in Naval Town."

Sally was not called upon to answer this. There came a cry from the distant courtyard and both began to walk quickly towards the steps. One of the servants was leaning over the courtyard wall, smiling and gesticulating.

"The *señora* is awake and wishes to see you, Don Marcus. She says she cannot wait!"

"I'll come!"

Sally drew back from the hand he had lifted to her elbow. "I'll stay out here for a while longer. Please, Marcus."

"All right, but don't start tiring yourself with worry. I'll arrange that you see Doña Inez during the evening for just two minutes." He gave her arm a friendly squeeze and strode on. No doubt he mounted the steps at a long lope, but Sally didn't linger to watch. She followed the paths through the cypress trees until she couldn't see the house at all, and then she stopped and sank down on to the grass.

She lay back and closed her eyes, felt coins of warmth from the dappled sunlight and heard the sweet note of a bird near by. Sally ached all over, and wondered why. Perhaps because the worst of the tension was over for a while, leaving her flat and exhausted.

She thought of the gracious Spanish house, with its courtyard and palms, its roses and magnolias, bougainvillias, oleanders and massed beds of exotic flowers; of the vineyards that spread across the hillsides and the little houses where the grape farmers reared their large, healthy families. They rented their farms, and Marcus bought their grapes and turned them into the sparkling amber wine for which the island was famous. And somewhere beyond Las Viñas there were acres of budding lilacs; in two weeks, Marcus had informed them on the taxi ride, the blossoms would be full enough for picking and pressing; San Palos lilac essence was one of the rarest genuine perfumes in the world.

And she was engaged to the owner of all this. Engaged for three whole weeks — what do you think of that? Her heart felt like a ball of lead at the end of a plumbline and there was a raw salty feeling in her throat. Now it seemed as if she would not survive one day of the deception, let alone three weeks. It was absurd that she, nineteen-year-old Sally Sheppard, should be the intended bride of

Marcus Durant, who was thirty-two, rich and experienced. No doubt Marcus himself had reflected, with wry amusement, that he might have been luckier in the two women he had befriended; a more motherly and serious mother, and a daughter who was fledged and fairly sophisticated would have done nicely. Still, one couldn't order up one's complications; they happened, and a man made the best of them.

To Marcus, the next few weeks would be simply a period to be lived through and forgotten. To keep his aged and ailing grandmother happy he would have gone to greater lengths, no doubt. He saw the whole thing in terms of the old lady's health.

And that was the way she, Sally, would have to view it. She must place the present precarious state of Doña Inez's health a long way above her own happiness and modest ambitions. Looked at that way, the frightening situation might be just bearable.

It was quite some time before Sally stirred herself to go back to the house. She went into her large airy bedroom, slipped off her frock and washed in the adjoining bathroom. She got into a blue figured linen, pushed a wave or two into the soft honey-pale hair and used a little make-up.

When she returned to the courtyard her mother was there, talking animatedly with the woman who had wheeled out a shimmering tray of silver teaware. The servant was smiling and nodding her head, and when she saw Sally the smile became softer.

Looking at both English women, she said, "This is a wonderful day for us all. *Maravilloso!*" And her shoes whispered away across the flagstones.

"Now isn't that touching?" Viola appealed to Sally. "I always thought Latin servants were awfully dour, but these make one feel wanted and important. I wonder if they make good tea, though. That huge silver pot looks heavy. Will you pour, dear?"

Sally poured. Her mother sat near the wall and looked towards the trees. She was wearing a soft cream silk that made her appear young and prematurely grey, and the matching shoes, with their pointed toes and spiky heels, emphasized the slender neatness of her ankles and calves. As usual she wore no rings but her wedding ring, and her only other adornment was a small gold blob in each ear. Dressed simply, Viola always carried a look of distinction which even the lavender rinse left intact. Sometimes she made Sally feel inadequate.

Viola said, "There are several acres of gardens — did you know that? And we're only one mile from the nearest beach. Not that I care for beaches, but I do like to look at the sea sometimes, and the Mediterranean is quite as blue as one hopes, isn't it? What have you been doing this afternoon? That woman said you'd been in the garden for a long time with Marcus."

"Yes, I was. Doña Inez woke up and he was called indoors."

"I suppose he's still with her." Viola frowned anxiously. "I do hope I shan't have to see the old lady. Old people make me shiver, even rich ones."

Sally smiled faintly. "I think you may be spared. It's unlikely that she'll be allowed visitors."

"And we're strangers to her," Viola comforted herself. "Aren't you glad now that we bought half a dozen new frocks each? Marcus has several friends who have villas along the coast, and even if he can't entertain here because of the grandmother they're bound to invite us to their houses. And of course the staff at Naval Town will have social events. Did you hear the real names of Naval Town and Naval Bay? Quite unpronounceable, so you can't blame the Navy for giving them their own nicknames. Sally," turning upon her a sudden scrutiny, "what *has* been happening to you? You look . . . doped!"

"It's the sun," said Sally. "Would you like some more tea?"

It was always easy to divert Viola, but that moment of awareness in her mother made Sally careful. She spoke of the intense blue of the sky, of the yellow butterflies — fancy, butterflies in March! of the peace and warmth and the lengthening shadows.

The tea-things were taken away, the sun slipped out of sight and cooler air displaced the warmth, so that the ancient Sealyham shivered and plodded indoors. A clock in the house chimed six, and a distant bell sent a peal of music through the hills. And then Marcus came out.

He had changed into light slacks and a dark shirt which made him look foreign and handsome. He came and sat down near the table, stretched an indolent leg and smiled.

"Sorry you had to have tea alone on your first day, but I naturally had to have mine with Doña Inez. Haven't been bored, have you?"

"Certainly not," said Viola at once. "And how is your grandmother?"

"She can't talk much — it tires her. But she got in a few questions." He switched from the topic. "I've ordered wine out here. It's a little early, but as this is a special occasion I thought we'd open a bottle of our own best vintage."

"That's thoughtful of you, Marcus. Arriving here today has been almost like being fêted. I haven't felt so wanted since . . ." her voice quivered easily, but it remained quite bright, "well, for some time. You couldn't have been kinder if we were relations."

"It's not kindness but selfishness, because I like having you here," he said smoothly. "And I'd like to think we're going to be related, too."

"You would?" she said, mystified. "Do you mean in the business sense?"

"Here's the wine," said Sally swiftly.

Marcus thanked the servant, leaned forward and twisted the white-capped bottle in its nest of ice. He said pleasantly, "You're rather young to be my mother-in-law, Viola, but it's the way things sometimes happen. Will you mind?"

His casualness stunned Sally. It almost stunned Viola; she sat right back in her chair and gazed at him with limpid blue eyes, and then turned the gaze upon Sally, who was scarlet and averted.

"This isn't a joke, is it?" she queried. There was a moment of tense silence before Viola exclaimed, "You've kept it so dark!" And the moment was past.

Marcus was smiling, and uncorking the bottle. "I didn't want Sally to tell you herself. We only decided finally this afternoon."

"Finally?" echoed Viola. "Then you were more than friendly on the ship? It all seems so very sudden. Marcus, did you feel drawn to Sally from the beginning? Was that why you made me promise to write to you from Barcelona? I shouldn't probe into your affairs, I suppose, but really . . ." She paused, at a loss, then laughed, a little helplessly. "I didn't even know you were interested in each other that way. I quite felt there were possibilities between Sally and that dear boy who played the piano, but you, Marcus! Sally told me herself that you made her feel uneasy when you danced with her. Was that when you first . . . no! It's not my business."

He gave her a glass that sparkled gently, gave another to Sally and raised his own. "To all three of us," he said, "and to Doña Inez."

Viola sipped, her glance upon him. "Does she know — your grandmother?"

He nodded. "She's delighted — wants to meet you both as soon as possible. I told her she could see Sally for a minute or two this evening, and that you would look in tomorrow."

"Oh." For a minute it seemed as if the unwanted meeting with the old *señora* had become more important to Viola than the news she had just heard. Then she sighed herself back to the present. "I do feel I should have known about this before. My only daughter falls in love with the most eligible man in the world, and I know nothing about it till she's actually engaged! I feel cheated."

"But you mustn't," said Sally, not very steadily. "After all, it's not quite a fortnight since we first met Marcus. And there was nothing to tell till today."

Viola sounded a little disconsolate as she answered, "I do understand. These things steal up on one so quickly, and it was really most thoughtful of Marcus to propose immediately we'd arrived, even though he may have thought it a little too early, because now we know our position in San Palos. You can't do any nursing, of course, darling, but I should think I could still go into business. Couldn't I, Marcus? I'd like to have an interest and a small income of my own."

"It can all be arranged,"said Marcus. The glance he sent across to Sally said, "What did I tell you? She's accepted it like a child." He took more of his drink. "There's just one thing, Viola. Doña Inez is not a modern, and for that reason I didn't tell her that Sally and I had known each other only for a short time. She assumed that I've known you both for a year or two in England, and I let her go on thinking that way. Anything you might say to the contrary could easily get through to her and perhaps disturb her, so will you be careful not to mention our short acquaintanceship?"

"Of course I will. I'll say nothing whatsoever about it to anyone, and if people are nosy I'll be vague!" Distinctly pleased with herself, Viola added, "I do realize you both let me into things as soon as you could. How long an engagement do you plan?"

"Mother . . ."

"We're not sure," said Marcus nonchalantly. "Exploring personalities takes time."

"Naturally. How soon may I put an announcement in *The Times*?"

Marcus smiled, and in that moment the whole thing, the pain as well as the strange excitement, fell into perspective for Sally. Either she must treat this lightly or get into a frightful state over it every time it was mentioned; and seeing that the old *señora* and her mother had accepted the engagement without question, the light treatment was her only course. She lifted her head, smiled with a creditable attempt at cheerfulness and said,

"That's for me to say, isn't it? I want to get used to having a fiancé before I see it in black and white!"

"Naughty," said Viola, and she laughed. She raised her glass once more. "To my two dear ones," she said sentimentally. "I couldn't be happier."

Marcus sat quite relaxed, smiling enigmatically upon the scene he had produced. Sally, looking at him, wondered what he was thinking. She thought his expression changed a fraction, that a faint bitterness sharpened the smile. Was he reflecting how different this could have been had the right woman been sitting where Sally now sat? He must hate this as much as she did, perhaps even more, because if Viola Sheppard and her daughter had not slipped into his life on the "Bellesta" he wouldn't now be living a sham. He would have come home to San Palos alone, have soothed the disappointed *señora* and got back into his former way of life. Instead of which he was living an outward happiness as well as the inward bitterness of losing a woman he had loved . . . perhaps still loved.

She became conscious that he was watching her and smiling sardonically. Her small pointed chin lifted to answer his challenge; not for anything would she have him guess what was happening to her heart.

CHAPTER THREE

DONA INEZ occupied the enormous bedroom on the corner of the house which was farthest from the entrance. There were balconies on two sides, each giving a view of the gardens and distant hills, and from one of them a flight of steps gave access to a small private patio which was enclosed by pergolas smothered with roses. It was through this patio that Sally approached the bedroom with Marcus.

It was dark now, and when they arrived in the balcony lights came on, and Sally saw the white, gold and pink bedroom softly and completely illuminated by wall lamps which were delicately shaded by ruched pink silk. The vast bed, its white carved headpiece touched with gold on the leaves and flowers, was covered by a light pink silk counterpane which was neatly turned back so that nothing but fine, perfumed linen touched the old lady who sat, a small figure in a white Shetland wool bed-jacket, in a nest of pillows.

Doña Inez was a legend on San Palos, and tiny and emaciated though she had now become, she was very much aware of the fact. Her hair, thin and white but beautifully piled up to make the most of it, must once have been black and lustrous, and the lovely framework of her face, stark now and overlaid by a yellowing, wrinkled skin, had certainly been arresting until a few years ago. Her hands were bony and clawlike, her shoulders sharp under the white wool, and at first view, from the balcony doorway, Sally's reaction was one of immense compassion. Small, isolated, old, she couldn't have much time left, and the task Sally had assumed wasn't really big when one considered the long lifetime of loves and happiness and griefs that this indomitable little woman represented.

Not that Doña Inez was pitiable. Good heavens, those eyes! They were fierce little coals, moving hardly at all but taking in everything.

Marcus led Sally to the side of the bed. "*Madrecita*, this is Sally. You are not to say more than *bienvenida*. You understand?"

The old lady's look at him was baleful. "You will not dictate, Marcus," she said in a hoarse, firm little voice. "In the house and vineyards you are the master, but not in this room." She gestured to Sally. "Come to the other side of the bed so that I can see you clearly. So." She stared unblinkingly at the flawless young face, the graceful neck and shoulders. "How old are you?"

Marcus said mildly, "I told you there was to be no inquisition till you're quite well. Sally's nineteen and very sensible."

"When I married," stated Doña Inez, "I was eighteen and not at all sensible. I insisted on marrying an Englishman whose yacht had foundered near San Palos in a storm. When I inherited Las Viñas this husband of mine turned our pleasant old estate into a business proposition. That is an Englishman for you!" But she cast a proud smile at Marcus before looking up once more at Sally's healthy pink cheeks. "It is good to be young and in love, no?"

"Very good, *señora*," said Sally without a tremor.

"You feel you are capable of making a man as masterful as my grandson a good wife? But perhaps that is not a fair question; for the moment it is enough to have decided. There is one thing for which I have to thank you, *señorita*."

"Leave it," said Marcus. "You're getting breathless again."

"I am not! I have rested expressly for the purpose of this talk. *Señorita*," directing that burning glance upwards once more, "I am very pleased you refused to marry Marcus in England. Knowing him a little, you will believe me when I tell you that at no time would he give us details about you, except that you were beautiful and willing to be his wife. So you will pardon me if I am inquisitive."

44

Again Marcus spoke before Sally could answer. "You promised not to talk much. Sally has been receiving new impressions all day, and she's tired. It's late for you, also."

"The child is young," said Doña Inez, "and the young are never tired. I have been sleeping all day. So I am permitted to speak in my own room?" She went on in her regal manner, "If you find me curious during the next few days you must forgive me, *señorita*. I wish to know you, that is all. Please convey to your good mother my regret that I am unable to welcome her as I should. Tomorrow we shall meet, and later she and I will arrange the details of the wedding."

"And now," said Marcus, "we'll say goodnight."

Her smile at him had become soft and loving. "You have made me very happy today — happier than I have been for many years. This *novia* you have chosen is quiet and pretty, and I look forward to spending some time with her each day, so that we may soon know each other. At this moment, perhaps, she is a little afraid of me, but you will convince her that there is no need for fear. On the contrary, I could not love any woman more than I would love your wife, Marcus."

His expression remained cool and soothing. "I know that. And now compose yourself. I'll call Katarina."

"Not for a moment." She pointed a small yellow stick of a finger at Sally's hand. "You have not exchanged rings? How is that?"

"We'll get round to it," Marcus said patiently. "When you awoke this morning you didn't even know I was on my way, yet here you are, wanting everything to happen at once. If you're worn out tomorrow I'll have Carlos on my neck."

"But the ring is important to a woman, if not to you. Soon you must choose which of the family rings you will use for the exchange, but now . . . give me my jewel-box, Marcus."

"I'll do no such thing. You've had enough excitement."

"I — am — not — excited," she said, spacing the words for emphasis. "I will not have the child under this roof

45

one night before presenting her with a token of our family affection. Give me the box."

"Oh, but please," said Sally, distressed. "I'd much rather not . . ."

"Katarina!" cried the old lady sharply.

The woman appeared magically at the inner doorway. *"Señora?"*

"My jewel-box, Katarina." The inlaid mahogany casket was swiftly placed on the sheet between her hands, and as Doña Inez opened it she gazed, narrow-eyed, at Marcus. "Do not look so disdainful of these things, my son. This little sapphire is a gift from me to your *novia,* but I wish her to wear it on the correct finger until we have chosen the betrothal ring. You yourself will put it there."

Marcus' smile was an aloof mask. "Very well — later. Give it to me."

The old *señora* placed the ring in his palm. "Do it soon — tonight. I confess I am a little weary, but before you go I wish to give you both my blessing. Please take your little Sally's hand across my bed."

He stood, tall and self-possessed, and looked across at Sally, stretched his hand to her. Tautly she responded, felt the firm grip on her fingers before the cool, bony hands of the old *señora* were clasped about the two that were locked together. Within a minute it was over and Sally had regained possession of her hand.

"Goodnight, my dear," Doña Inez was saying, a little weakly. "You have made me so happy . . . so very happy. We will talk . . . tomorrow."

"Goodnight, *señora,*" Sally whispered.

Marcus bent and touched his lips to the lined forehead. "It's good to be back with you," he said quietly. "Sleep well."

The bright old eyes in the weary face looked at him serenely. *"Querido mio,"* she said. "I knew that even in this matter which is close to your heart I could depend on you. Goodnight."

Sally walked out the way she had come. She knew Marcus had reached her side, but she couldn't look at him.

As she descended the steps her knees bent stiffly, but she was only three steps from the *patio* when she stumbled. She flung out a hand to grab at the narrow wrought-iron balustrade, caught it but hooked on to a swaying trailer of rose stem at the same time as Marcus steadied her at the other side. Pain shot through the palm of her hand and involuntarily she let out a small cry.

"Hurt yourself?" he asked quickly.

"It's nothing — just a scratch. There's plenty of light — I should have watched the steps."

As they reached the patio he whipped a handkerchief from his pocket, took her hand and dabbed at the splash of blood. "Didn't grab a thorn, did you? Sure of that?"

Tremulously she said, "Yes, I'm sure. Please let go of my hand, Marcus."

But his hold tightened. "Don't take fright, there's a good girl. You did very well up there. The *señora* will sleep soundly tonight."

"I'm glad."

"Don't get wound up about it, please. If I haven't been absolutely frank with you it's because I felt we should keep this thing as impersonal as possible. Some time you may have to see Doña Inez alone, and I think there are one or two things I'd better tell you, before that happens." She stood, small and straight and a little pale in the muted light from the windows, saying nothing. So he tugged gently at the wrist he held and added, "You're helping me in something that I feel is very necessary just now, and worth while. We can depend on Carlos Suarez, as my grandmother's doctor, to slow down her natural impulses. You'll have to take the talk of celebrations and a wedding in your stride. If you were in love with me — I mean if you had a crush as a girl sometimes does on a man who's older — it would make things awkward and uncomfortable for us both. But you haven't, thank heaven; you even feel a little enmity for me, though I can't think why. Still, perhaps it's as well." He paused and looked at her speculatively. "Anything in particular you'd like to know about things here, and me?"

She shook her head. "I'd rather not know anything at all."

A smile made his voice slightly mocking. "That's not true. I saw the little daggers come into your eyes when Doña Inez thanked you for not marrying me in England. That's what you hate most about this situation, isn't it? The fact that you're being mistaken for someone else?" He shrugged and tacked on laconically, "You'd better hear about it."

"I've naturally gathered that you were engaged to someone in England," she said offhandedly. "Perhaps I hadn't better be told any more than that."

"It's important that you realize where you stand," he said. "The engagement existed, but it wasn't official, in any sense. She's an actress — not a particularly good one, but quite lovely and sparkling. She had a small part in a West End play, and it was understood between us that I'd be there when the play came off and would arrange to bring her here. When I got to London she told me the play was going to America and she had the chance to go with it. So that was that."

"She broke it off, as casually as that?"

His shoulders lifted in a half foreign gesture. "I dare say she thought she could have the glamor and me too. She sailed within three days. I went to stay with friends in Yorkshire, but there was nothing to keep me in England, so I came home." He closed her fingers over the handkerchief wadded in her palm. "I made my first questionable decision when I chose the cruise instead of returning as usual by air. However, you and I met and McCartney spread the glad news . . . and here we are, temporary fiancés."

She lowered her head. "You seem oddly unmoved by what happened to you in England. Yet it must have been a blow."

"It didn't happen catastrophically." He sounded cynical as he went on, "Even as we parted Nadine told me she was desperately in love with me. She also said that if I loved

48

her I'd let her have the wonderful experience of acting in America before we married."

"That could be true."

"Not for me," in hard tones. "The woman I marry will consider me first, right from the start. Still, I'm grateful to Nadine Carmody. She's completely put me off English women." He smiled, quite charmingly. "That doesn't include you and your mother, Sally Sheppard. I may marry a Spaniard, but I'm pretty sure no Spanish woman would do for me what you yourself are doing for me now."

"You saved us from a nasty predicament in Barcelona," she said coolly, "and you've promised to help us become established here. It's an exchange of favors, that's all." She hesitated. "I'm horribly afraid that when your grandmother hears the truth she'll have a relapse."

"We'll guard against that. When she's a little stronger you'll have to seem restive, as though living here in the house doesn't suit you. I'll find you a villa that you can share with your mother. That way, you can gradually break off seeing Doña Inez, and when she's more or less prepared for it, I'll tell her you feel you're not sufficiently in love to marry."

"She'll . . . hate me."

"It's possible, but there's already been groundwork in that direction." With a shrug and a very slight movement away from her he said, "My father was her son, and much more Spanish than I am. He married an English woman who could never properly settle here. They separated when I was very young and she never came back. So you see," with a sardonic smile, "Doña Inez will only be grateful that you found out before marriage, instead of after as my mother did."

Sally was pensive. "It doesn't seem quite fair that she should think badly of all English women, does it? I suppose she's always wanted you to marry a Spanish girl?"

"She pegged away at it for a few years. Spanish women are very beautiful and when they're young they're spirited, but I always felt they were too immersed in their homes, too docile in marrige, to make exciting wives. But with time, one's ideas tend to change."

"You mean you no longer want an exciting wife?"

His eyes narrowed in the way his grandmother's did, and he spoke a little crisply. "We seem to have got away from the point, don't we? I merely wanted you to know that no one here has ever been aware of the name and profession of the woman I was engaged to. All that side of the business is between you and me and no one else. For all practical purposes here, you're she."

"I understand."

"I hope so." His voice had roughened. "This is your first day here and already you've shown both hurt and anger. I don't want you to be hurt in any way."

She lifted a hand. "A little of it is inevitable, but," with a light smile, "I won't let it go deep. There's one thing you haven't covered. You're the best-known man on San Palos and for two or three weeks I shall be paired with you in people's minds. After that, you can go off and scout round for your Spanish girl; and what shall I be permitted to do — stay on the island and take up nursing? Wouldn't that rather cramp your style?"

"We'll deal with that when the time comes." He seemed to have changed position, so that the lights of the house were behind him and the planes of his face were obscured by shadow. Quite gently, he touched her arm. "It would help no end if you'd try to get into holiday mood and find fun in the situation. I promise you I'll tone things down whenever I can, but there is the matter of this ring." It glinted in the palm of his left hand, and as she jerked back from it he said, "It's a dress ring that Doña Inez used to wear when she was young; it never belonged to my mother. I want you to take care of it and slip it on whenever you go in to see Doña Inez."

She moistened her lower lip. Then with a show of nonchalance she took the ring, looked at it for a moment and dropped it into the wide triangular pocket of her skirt. "Very well, Marcus. After all, if one's playing a part one may as well do it properly. I'm sure your former fiancée

50

could have managed this role more successfully, but I'll never let it be said that I didn't give it a good try."

He didn't like that, but she hadn't meant him to. The hand on her arm was less gentle as it moved up to clasp her elbow. "Let's go in. Carlos will have arrived for dinner, and your mother is bound to be sentimental. No wisecracks, if you don't mind!"

Momentarily, Sally wondered if she'd imagined that faint movement in the balcony above. They were bound to be watched, though; she would have to get used to it.

*   *   *

The following few days put Sally into a strangely bemused state from which even her mother's pertinent questions only partially roused her. Perhaps the fact that life at Las Viñas followed a somewhat conventional pattern contributed to her static frame of mind. Every morning started the same: coffee and crisp golden twists of bread with balls of yellow butter and delicate silver shells filled with marmalade and honey, all served in her bedroom on a silver tray garnished with a single spray of lilac — this being the white and lilac bedroom, she supposed. Viola said that on different mornings she'd had cornflowers, delphinium and scabious on her breakfast tray; because her room was blue and white, no doubt.

Lunch was eaten at the table in the courtyard, tea could be served wherever one wanted it, and dinner, a seven-course meal accompanied by wines, was always served in ceremonial fashion in the dining room which was pleasingly furnished in seventeenth-century Spanish provincial style.

The *sala,* a long room which looked into the cloisters and was really rather grand, with its portraits and landscapes and inlaid tables and damask chairs, seemed to be used only in the evening, for cocktails before dinner and coffee after it. There was usually a guest or two for dinner.

Sally found herself drawn quite smoothly into the set-up. After the first day or so she accepted felicitations with a calm smile. Marcus saw to it that she was not called upon to converse at length with any one person, and through his debonair and ever-present care Sally had surprisingly little to contend with. Privately she wondered if he trusted her, and almost decided that he didn't.

In the matter of Doña Inez, for instance. He had told Sally she would probably have to see the old *señora* alone, but after reflection had obviously concluded it might be dangerous. So every morning at ten-thirty he went with Sally into that large beautiful bedroom, and there he talked just enough to prevent Sally from talking at all, and fifteen minutes later he would insist that they had been long enough in the room. Doña Inez would protest and he would lift an eyebrow and say carelessly, "There's plenty of time. We want you strong and well again before we start making plans." His way of keeping a fiancée in view but managing to stay clear of consolidation was clever, of course. If that wily old woman his grandmother suspected anything, she was lulled by the sight of her own sparkling sapphire on Sally's finger; Sally often saw that bright, piercing glance resting tranquilly on her left hand.

Viola, Sally was both amused and chagrined to discover, delightedly accepted the engagement as a sequel to her own warm friendship with Marcus on the "Bellesta." Had she been younger he would have chosen herself, but in the circumstances he had done the next best thing, and Viola was the last person to be jealous of her own daughter. After all, so long as between them they brought Marcus and his money into the family, what did it matter? He was experienced and charming, very considerate and overwhelmingly anxious to take care of their future; and what good luck that he felt Sally would suit him as a wife!

"Just knowing that we have such a man to depend on has made my heart light as air," she said, and added ingenuously, "I'm really most easily satisfied, you know. So long as I don't have to worry about money and there's a man in the family I'm the happiest person in the world."

Sally decided not to comment upon this. If her mother decided to remain on San Palos more or less indefinitely she would always have Marcus in the background. And already she had been down to Naval Town and looked over the possibilities of starting some small business which could be run on little capital and plenty of feminine charm. Since leaving England she had improved so much in health and outlook that Sally felt her own problems to be negligible. They had come to the Mediterranean for Viola's sake, and for Viola's sake Sally would endure anything. And there was one thing of which Sally was very certain; after the disastrous business in Barcelona this island of San Palos must seem very like heaven to her mother.

Sally found it easy to be friendly with Dr. Carlos Suarez. He was the dedicated type and peculiarly suited to the rather unconventional ways of the island. It was on her fourth day, just after he had seen Doña Inez and pronounced her quite remarkably improved, that he paused in the courtyard to speak to Sally, who sat there with an unread book open on her lap.

"Good morning," he said, in his polite smiling tones. "You are again admiring the view?"

She closed her book and placed it on the table. "I shall have to give it up; it's like a drug. The trouble is, I've so little to do."

"Marcus will surely find interests for you; and as you know, I shall be most pleased to conduct you through our little hospital."

"I'd be so glad if you would," she said. "You see, I was doing nursing just before we left England, and it would be wonderful to start working again."

Carlos, thin and dark and looking a little more than his forty years, smiled incredulously. "But that is splendid! The hospital needs such a patroness — one who understands how such a place is conducted, and the problems of the staff." He hesitated. "Are you free until lunchtime?"

"You mean may I go with you now? I'd love it."

"Then come. It will make me most happy to introduce you to everyone!"

"But not as a patroness, please," she said, as she moved at his side. "Just tell everyone that I'm a second-year nurse and would love to work with them."

"I am afraid it is already known that you are the fiancée of Marcus Durant, but they will be pleased to learn that you chose to be a nurse." He almost stopped as he asked, "You do not wish to advise your mother of where you are going?"

"She's out with Marcus. They're having a sort of meeting with the man who owns the department store in Naval Town."

"Captain Northwick?"

"Is that his name? Is he a naval man too?"

"Retired, but he likes the naval atmosphere." Carlos opened the door of his modest black car and saw Sally seated before getting behind the wheel. "You have acted as a splendid tonic upon Doña Inez. Do you know that?"

"Yes."

"A week ago she could hardly speak, but this morning it was difficult to keep her quiet. Already she is impatient to get up for a little while each day."

"Is she fit enough?"

"Yes, but I shall not allow it yet. Katarina has instructions about gentle massage of the legs." He smiled at her as they drove off. "Until you are married to Marcus and in a position to make rules in the house, you will not be permitted to help in the nursing of Doña Inez. Katarina is very jealous of her rights and privileges, and I must say she has shown the utmost care and devotion. Even as the wife of Marcus you will have difficulty in supplanting Katarina."

"I wouldn't try." She changed the subject. "Since I arrived I haven't left Las Viñas. You must explain things to me as we drive."

For part of the way they were on the road by which Sally had come to Las Viñas. She saw the orderly acres of vine-laden pergolas, the little houses with their fruit trees and vegetable gardens, and more vines, with here and there an ancient fig or olive left standing. Rest-trees, the islanders called them, and Carlos slowed so that by looking through an avenue of grapevines Sally could see baskets of food and rolled jackets in the shade of one of them.

They came down almost to coast level, and here the houses were more numerous, their gardens more spectacular. They had left the road to the harbor and were winding through a long village, at the end of which, hidden except for its bell-tower and part of a curly pink-tiled roof, stood the Casa de Curacion.

"This is the name it was given two hundred years ago, when a few members of a sisterhood began their work in a wooden house on the site. The house of healing has now become an important part of the island," said Carlos. "The building you will see as we go along the drive is the main nursing home. To the right there is a new block which was built at the expense of the naval authorities for their staff and families. I will take you there first."

The following hour was the most satisfying Sally had spent since arriving on the island. She toured the little modern building and enjoyed the usual jokes with one or two of the nurses, went on with Carlos to the main building, which was ornate in architecture but clinically perfect. The Sisters moved swiftly along the corridors in their blue and white habits, smiled at Carlos and shook Sally's hand with hearty firmness. Sally saw the patients only from doorways; all were islanders. Except one.

They saw him in the wide sheltered veranda as they came out of the building by the front entrance. He wore black trousers and a flowing silk shirt and a very white bandage about his head. Above the bandage were thick, glossy black curls and below it a pair of laughing dark eyes enlivened by a sallow handsome face. He was about twenty-eight, patently bored and apparently friendly with Carlos, for he straightened from his lounging position near one of the fluted white pillars and moved towards them as they stopped in the veranda. Sally felt the young man's bold, raking glance upon her as he bowed before speaking to the doctor.

"Pardon, please . . . have you spoken to him yet, Carlos?"

Carlos frowned and shook his head. "I have not seen him today." And then, correctly, "Permit me. This is Josef Carvallo . . . Miss Sheppard, who is the fiancée of Marcus."

The change in the young man's expression was swift and startling. He gave Sally a long, brilliant stare, bowed again and bore her hand to his lips; and he wasn't in a hurry to release the hand either.

Earnestly he said, "You are staying at Las Viñas, señorita?"

"Yes, I am."

"Then perhaps you could do for me this thing that Carlos is too busy to do."

The doctor said, "It isn't necessary to bother the señorita, Josef. I will see Marcus as soon as possible."

"But Señorita Sheppard will see him sooner, no?"

Before Sally could make a reply fate took a hand. A Sister called the doctor urgently, from the doorway, and Carlos excused himself and begged that Sally would sit in the car till he could join her. She smiled at the young man as though in farewell, but very gently, very politely, he laid a hand on her arm to detain her.

"I will not keep you long," he said. "As you see, I have had an accident. It is not serious — a gash which had to be stitched — but I cannot leave the hospital because I have no home here." He paused, and the shining dark glance rested once more on her fair young face. "In a very distant way, through my mother, I am related to Marcus, though not to Carlos. I am anxious to see Marcus — can you arrange that for me?"

"I can mention it to him," she said. "How did you hurt your head?"

His smile was mournful and mischievous. "In a brawl, I am afraid. It was at the hotel last night, only a few minutes after I had arrived in San Palos. I had a small disagreement with someone and he was a heavier man than I. I woke up early this morning in a ward here, and for breakfast I had pain in the head and a strong lecture from

Carlos. You see, I am the black sheep of two or three families."

She had to smile back at him. "Does that make you very black?"

"Unfortunately, yes." His frank disturbing gaze again settled upon Sally. "You are really the fiancée of Marcus? I cannot believe it."

"Why not?" she asked carefully.

He shrugged. "You are not his kind of woman. You are just a girl, and I would say you should marry someone young and gay and very ardent. You yourself are young, but you are sober because of this engagement which demands too much of you."

She wondered if he really saw a little way below the surface or whether it was a line he had decided upon. She said calmly, "You're presuming to know too much on so short an acquaintance, Señor Carvallo. I'll tell Marcus you want to see him."

"Please do not go," he begged. "I had no wish to offend you. If I do not see you as a suitable wife for Marcus you must blame my faulty powers of deduction. Marcus is a most fortunate man, but then in everything he has always been fortunate. I," with a pathetic brush of the hand over his bandage, "have always been the victim of atrocious luck."

"I think it's possible that you go out of your way to attract it," she said. "Don't you live on San Palos?"

He shook his head ruefully. "I live nowhere. I have been everywhere, even to your cold England, but I cannot settle. In that mood, I am happiest here on San Palos."

"Do you always stay at the hotel?"

His smile was conspiratorial. "I start there, always. Then I meet Marcus and he invites me to Las Viñas. That is what I am hoping for now — even more," with a kindling in his eyes, "since I have met you."

"Marcus may not want more guests. His grandmother has been seriously ill."

"But I am no trouble," he declared warmly, "and I adore Doña Inez as if she were my own grandmother." Almost boyishly he tacked on, "She likes me, you know. There is always a little fondness in old people for black sheep."

Sally found herself laughing against her will. "You'd better keep the bandage round your head until you've seen Marcus. It may soften him."

"Could you not permit me to go back with you now, for lunch?"

"No, but I promise I'll tell him. And I think you'd better sit down. You probably lost some blood — you're pale."

"You think I look ill?" he asked urgently. "Perhaps I can depend on you to approach Marcus for me — ask that he will allow me to spend a few more days of convalescence at Las Viñas?"

"I'll mention it to Marcus. And now, please sit down. I'm going to the doctor's car."

She gave him a distant nod and resolutely walked to the black saloon. For several minutes she sat looking ahead, at a bed of budding roses backed by giant oleanders. Then, almost without volition, she looked up at the veranda. Josef Carvallo was still there, leaning on the wall and staring down at her. He was ashen and the bandage made him look ill and somehow neglected. But his smile, when he caught her glance, was merry and companionable. He'd probably stood there willing her to look his way and felt mighty proud of himself when she'd done so! Crossly, she turned her head and looked down towards the gates. By the time Carlos arrived, full of apologies, she was able to convince herself that the young man on the veranda was just an attractive cad.

As it happened, Carlos confirmed this conclusion. "Josef has been coming to San Palos since he was a schoolboy," he told Sally. "At first it was to Las Viñas, for holidays, and then he would arrive whenever he felt inclined. Two years ago he came to settle; he worked as a superintendent throughout the harvest and wine-making, but as soon as the wine *fiesta* was over he went away again, after wrecking a betrothal between two members of good families here; he bewitched the girl and she would not marry."

"Good heavens. What happened to her?"

"She teaches at a convent. Josef came back last year and the girl would not even look at him, which proves," with a quiet laugh, "that his influence is not lasting. Perhaps that girl will yet marry her former fiancé."

"How does he live — Josef?"

"He has a small allowance, and to supplement it he works occasionally. I believe that among other things he has been a journalist, a painter of ceramics and a hack violinist."

"Sounds a little as if he were creative. Can't he be helped in some way?"

Carlos shrugged. "Marcus has helped him many times, and you cannot wonder that he has grown impatient. Josef is ungrateful and without regrets. He comes now to San Palos because he is penniless and wants a new start."

"And he begins by getting into a fight," she said. "He doesn't look at all well, does he?"

"He has been taking no care of himself," said Carlos with a sigh. "For a very few years the body can tolerate an amount of wild living, but there arrives a time when a man must come to his senses and slow down. In years, Josef is young; but physically he is much older. Even last year his general condition was much sounder than it is now. It is time that one took him in hand. Only Marcus is capable of it, and after the wrecking of that engagement he said he would do no more for Josef."

"You said that was two years ago. What happened last year?"

"Josef arrived while Marcus was away in England. He stayed only a week or two."

Sally said pensively, "I suppose he's never grown up because nothing has ever touched him closely. I promised him that I'd speak to Marcus for him."

"That is good," with the quiet, admiring smile. "Josef was fortunate in meeting you today; if you cannot persuade Marcus to make one more attempt for this young man, no one can."

But Sally had no illusions. "I can try, anyway," she murmured. "Thank you very much for taking me down to the nursing home, Dr. Suarez."

"We are almost cousins. Please call me Carlos," he said. "The Casa de Curacion is not like your English hospital, I am sure!"

"It's a little like a cottage hospital, I suppose. I'd love to work there. Do you take second-years?"

"But, my dear *señorita* . . ."

"I only meant, do you take them?" she said lightly.

"We do not train nurses," he said. "We have fully trained staff and some nursing assistants who are generally older island women; the assistants do work which is normally done by probationers. We have no facilities for training nurses."

"So you'd find it difficult to place a second-year?"

"Not at all," he answered. "The Sister in charge of the British block would plan the duties of a second-year nurse and she would be a member of the permanent staff for as long as it satisfied her to remain with us. We are too short of staff ever to turn away anyone who could help."

Momentarily Sally felt an overwhelming nostalgia for the big bleak corridors of St. Alun's, for the moments of apprehension and hysterical laughter, of quietness and reward. Then they were sweeping along the drive of Las Viñas and the car was halting at the foot of the steps which wound up to the courtyard.

Carlos got out of the car with her, bent over her hand. "I am a doctor and you set out to be a nurse. I feel we have a small bond, you and I."

"I feel it too," she said. "I'd like to go to the hospital again some time, when you're free. Thank you very much, Carlos."

"It was my pleasure." He looked up, called cheerfully, "Ah, Marcus! You have heard my report about the *señora* from Katarina?"

Marcus nodded, and said offhandedly, "Are you coming up here for lunch?"

"Unfortunately, no. I still have a call to make. Till tomorrow!"

Sally reached the top of the steps just as Carlos drove away down the drive. Marcus was alone, and had apparently been writing something at the table when he heard the car, for an ashtray held down a couple of envelopes while the writing pad flapped gently in the breeze. He looked at her from under his thick dark brows. The eagle-like quality in him was so pronounced that Sally knew, fearfully, that he was in an inflexible mood. And it came to her, suddenly, that this man who could manage anything and anyone was capable of violence.

Warily she said, "Your cousin was good enough to take me to the nursing home. I had a most interesting hour there."

"Why didn't you tell a servant where you were going?"

"Was it necessary? I didn't even think of it."

"We were invited down to Northwick's house for lunch. I left your mother there and came here to fetch you."

"Well, I couldn't have foreseen that, could I?" She looked at her watch. "It's not quite one. I could change in five minutes."

"All right. Get busy."

His uncompromising tone was chilling. Without looking at him again Sally went into the dim, flower-smelling hall and up the beautiful old staircase to her bedroom. Quickly she washed and changed into a tan and white glazed cotton, made up a little and grabbed a handkerchief. When she came out into the courtyard Marcus was sealing a letter and one of the maids was waiting to take it.

Marcus said, in the pleasant voice he always used when speaking to servants, "It's not urgent, Carmelita — any time this afternoon. We shan't be in for lunch."

"But there will be eight for dinner, señor?"

"I think so. And be sure that the bedroom you prepare for Don Josef is some way from the señora's room. You understand that whoever takes this letter down to the nursing home must wait for Señor Carvallo and drive him back?"

"Yes, *señor*."

He nodded and the servant went into the house. He took Sally's elbow and descended the steps with her, put her into the front seat of the blue saloon and set the car rolling down the winding drive. Her first impulse was to put a question about Josef. Marcus couldn't have seen the young man since she herself had seen him, and yet she had found him writing a note of invitation and making preparations for Josef's stay at Las Viñas. Still, Marcus didn't look as if he'd take kindly to being questioned about his actions, and in any case it wasn't difficult to work out what must have happened. Marcus had been into Naval Town this morning; he would have heard of the brawl and Josef's removal to hospital. Distasteful though he might find it, as head of the family it was his business to take charge of Josef and his peccadilloes on San Palos. Sally decided to say nothing at all.

But as they neared the sea, Marcus asked, "What did you do at the nursing home?"

"I walked through some of the wards."

"In the British section?"

"Yes, and in the main building. I've never before been in a hospital run by Sisters. Carlos seemed to think they'd be able to find a place for me on the staff."

"You asked him *that*?" he demanded sharply.

"Of course not," she replied hastily. "I only made sort of . . . interested enquiries. You did say that it wouldn't matter if Carlos knew the truth about us."

"I've changed my mind. A young connection of mine, Josef Carvallo, is likely to be grounded at Las Viñas for a while, and for the duration of his stay I insist that we maintain the fiction."

"You said we could trust Carlos—and I'm sure of it. He's a doctor and he's kind and . . ."

"And he's attracted to you."

"To me?" Sally gave him a long surprised stare. "What in the world makes you think that?"

He shrugged. "I grew up with Carlos—give me credit for knowing him. When we arrived he was looking in to see Doña Inez at seven o'clock each morning before going down to the hospital. Now it's ten, when you're more likely to be about. He's twice your age and he doesn't consciously think of you as a woman—because ostensibly you belong to me—but he's a Spaniard, and he's not going to deny himself the pleasure of seeing you often and sharing that part of you that's the nurse." This apparently left her speechless, and he added, "You like Carlos very much, don't you?"

"Of course I do. He's the first doctor, except our old Dr. Mowbray, who hasn't scared me stiff."

"Leave Carlos till you're free," he said. "The situation is sufficiently complex as it is, but while you're officially tied to me we can handle it easily, so long as you don't confuse matters by forgetting the main issue."

"I'm hardly likely to forget that"

"Good," he said flatly. "I certainly don't want to be driven to stern measures."

"Oh, you don't!" she flashed, but almost at once her anger evaporated and she sighed. "I'm sorry. I used to get it in the neck sometimes at St. Alun's for being impatient. I just wish it were a month from now, and everything were straight."

"Believe it or not," he said, his tone a little sharp with mockery, "so do I." The subject was dismissed as he waved a hand towards a row of square pink and white cottages.

"The last one is our destination. Inside, it's more nautical than the Navy itself. I expect your mother's reached the desperate stage."

The tiny square garden was a warning. Grass so close-grown that it looked like velvet, a straight gravel path symmetrically edged with giant sea-shells, and a ship's lantern of gleaming brass hanging beside the front window.

Marcus swung the cord of the ship's bell and a voice boomed, "Ah, so you're back at last. Come in, come in!"

63

CHAPTER FOUR

CHARLES NORTHWICK was a trim, stocky man with white well-brushed hair, thick white eyebrows and a ruddy complexion. In his light linen jacket and tobacco-brown trousers, the jacket sporting in the top pocket a dark brown handkerchief which matched his tie, he looked less a naval man than a prosperous business executive. But his sitting room echoed the nautical flavor of the entrance hall. The white walls were covered with prints of ships of every age and type, the few gaps being sprinkled with mementoes of the South Seas and the Arctic Ocean. The effect of those walls so overwhelming that one hardly noticed the staid leather upholstery of the chairs, the black refectory table, the dark patterned rugs. But for the off-white sail-cloth curtaining which was appliquéd with flowers, the room would have presented a scene of unrelieved gloom.

Viola, apparently, had long ago succumbed to the atmosphere. She sat in a chair, holding a glass of sherry in one hand and with the other nervously gripping the edge of a book which looked too massive for her lap to bear. As Marcus and Sally came in she let out a breath of pure pleasure and relief.

"I was terrified that something had happened to you on the road," she said. "The Colonel . . ."

"Captain, ma'am," she was corrected. "Never known much about the Army, never."

"I do apologize," said Viola, looking grateful as Marcus lifted the tome of old prints from her lap. "It must be the sherry on an empty . . ." She stopped and laughed confusedly. "Marcus, do rescue me. The Captain must think I'm a complete moron, and I did want to impress him favorably. The way I've been talking he'll never believe I could run a garden shop in his department store."

The Captain was gallant, however. "My dear Mrs. Sheppard, I'm convinced you're the woman to make a success

64

of the venture. You're decorative, you know a great deal about flowers and pot plants, and I feel sure that you would be only too happy to give advice to the young married women who comprise most of our customers. As you were saying a few minutes ago, it's time the Navy personnel began to order bouquets for birthdays and anniversaries and the flat-dwellers to decorate their balconies. I know nothing of such things—" with a courtly bow he gave Sally a glass of sherry and then turned to hand a whisky and soda to Marcus—"but it's like other departments of the store. I've chosen someone I felt was right for each section, and so far I haven't been disappointed in any of them. For the flowers, I feel that you are right, ma'am."

Viola smiled shakily. "I do wish you wouldn't keep calling me ma'am," she said plaintively. "After all, if you're engaging me it's more in keeping that I should call you sir."

Captain Northwick looked thoroughly shocked. "There is nothing of that kind in the Casa Northwick. Some of my assistants are island women and some of them are wives of naval ratings who are often away at sea. Even they do not call me sir! And you, who are almost a member of the Durant family, and a great lady, if I may say so, in your own right, will be doing us an immense honor by merely supervising this new department. Naturally, I will find an assistant for you and give you a free hand."

"San Palos is very small, you know," protested Viola, "and we can't be sure the garden department will be a financial success. As to my own qualifications, I ought to warn you that . . ."

Marcus said smoothly, "The Captain already understands your position, Viola. Your suggestion about turning his cosmetic counter into a small beauty salon didn't appeal to him because he'll never take make-up and titivating seriously."

The Captain nodded. "I'm afraid that's true. Can't bear enamelled women—can't bear 'em at all. You and your daughter are the two most beautiful women on this island— and the two most natural!"

"Why, thank you." Viola, who spent at least an hour each morning in front of her mirror selecting jars and bottles from a crystal array, was innocently pleased. "Isn't that a sweet compliment, Sally?"

"Charming," said Sally. "What happens if your garden department is a flop?"

The Captain smiled, and suddenly looked handsome. "It won't fail. Your mother has the personality and the touch; I'm sure of it. The idea has been at the back of my mind for some time, but it couldn't take shape because I had no one to handle it for me." Modestly, he added, "I started my store from a small shop which I bought from a Spaniard. It has grown on other people's brains, not mine."

"But the enterprise was yours," Marcus commented. "It's always surprised me that a naval man tucked away on the bridge should have such a good idea of character and personality in others. Even after several years of running the place I don't believe you know very much about it."

"That's true; I don't. In a town such as Barcelona or Birmingham I'd have gone broke within a year. Here on San Palos I've no competition and almost anything will sell as long as the price is right. And the whole establishment depends on other people, not on me."

"You're the King of Casa Northwick," stated Viola, in her pleased-with-herself manner. "They'd all go to pieces without their figurehead."

"You flatter me, ma'am . . . Mrs. Sheppard. But I hope that's true. And now we'll have lunch, shall we? My housekeeper is very patient, but I'm sure she's chafing. Allow me."

They edged into a small dining room that somehow held a long mahogany table, eight chairs, a chiffonier and a writing table as well as the inevitable naval odds and ends. The dinner was unimaginative; chicken soup, minced steak cutlets with vegetables and salad, and fruit tartlets. Sally saw her mother eyeing the swarthy little housekeeper and the plain, gold-rimmed china, the bone-handled knives, the unwinking glassware, the colored heatproof mats and the ancient pot of basil which had no doubt been set firmly in the centre of the dining table every day for the past five years. Viola, who could be put off her food by a knife set askew or a single green fly on the table flowers, valiantly tried a little of everything; she was determined not to upset the very worthy Captain Northwick.

He, Sally decided, was something of an anachronism and to some extent an odd man out. It seemed that his father had owned an old and respected bookshop in Chester, and that he himself had felt that such an establishment would suit him very well on retirement from the Navy. But by the time he was free he had decided to live close to the sea and preferably in a warm climate. For a start, and because the Navy had a base on San Palos, he had taken a room for a couple of months at Jim McCartney's hotel in Naval Town "just for a rest." The island had grown on him, but bookselling to such a community would hardly have kept him in tobacco. So when an old Spaniard had decided to sell his small general store the Captain took it on.

"Simply as a hobby," he explained genially. "I thought the place would show a small but sufficient return. The strange thing was that my own tastes in food and haberdashery made a success of it. I threw out all the junk and began to stock the sort of canned and packeted foods I like myself. They sold at once and I found myself with a long list of permanent customers among the naval personnel. So I bought up the shop next door, and filled it with occasional furniture; that was the beginning of the present furnishing department."

"How extraordinarily brave," remarked Viola, gazing wonderingly at the outsize chiffonier. "Did you furnish this house from your shop, Captain?"

"No, dear lady," he said proudly. "I ordered most of these things from a London store. Here, I couldn't sell good leather chairs and massive pieces of mahogany. These people live in cottages and flats."

Viola smiled gently; to anyone else she might have pointed out that this, too, was a cottage—but not to Captain Northwick the business man. "And gradually, during the past few years, you've added to your original shop till it's quite an emporium. Supposing the Navy decided to abandon this base?"

"I'm prepared for that. The store is prosperous and I don't live extravagantly. I'd give up and go on a world cruise. Financially, San Palos has made me more than secure."

"Well, you served the Navy for long enough," stated Marcus. "No one could blame you for getting rich on it, and Naval Town would have been a much duller place without the Casa Northwick."

At this point, Captain Northwick opened a bottle of champagne. His complexion became a little ruddier as he filled the glasses and he spoke almost shyly, standing and holding his own glass.

"Marcus, I want to congratulate you and wish you much happiness. Miss Sheppard . . . your health and good fortune."

"Well, how nice," said Viola chattily, and she sipped at the same time. "I thought you'd forgotten we had a newly engaged couple at the table, Captain."

He sat down quickly and shook his head. "I'm slow in these things, but it's not because they escape me. My experience of life has been one-sided."

"Limited to ships and shops?" she suggested lightly, and looked happy when he laughed. "I shall insist that you learn about flowers. And, Captain, if you honor me with another invitation to lunch, please put that old toby-jug over there somewhere where I can't see it and leave this mouldy grey plant behind the kitchen curtain, where it belongs. I'll bring you a posy myself!"

As they all moved back into the sober little drawing room Sally felt quite light-hearted. It was more than a year since her mother had displayed so much humor and spirit. No doubt at all that San Palos and these people suited her, and that the thought of running a gardening and florist's counter in the town cheered her tremendously.

The job was just right for her, Sally thought gratefully. The marvel was that Captain Charles Northwick had immediately seen that fact and more or less engaged her. There was a little more talk about it and before they left the cottage it had been arranged that Viola should go down to the store with the Captain as soon as possible to decide on a décor for her little bower.

Viola was enchanted with the whole idea, and said as much as Marcus drove them back to Las Viñas. "I'd far rather deal with plants and flowers than cosmetics, and flowers are so plentiful on the island that I'll always have abundant supplies of vastly different kinds. There's just one thing. Marcus, I've already seen island women with buckets and baths full of flowers. Do they sell in Naval Town?"

"Yes. Very cheaply. You can't compete with them; it wouldn't be right, anyway. You'll have to go for the expensive trade."

"Are they licensed?"

"No, but they're known. Your best bet would be to buy from them yourself—take their best stuff. I'll have a talk to some of the Navy men I know—if you can decorate the tables for their next big social affair, you're in."

"That would be splendid." Viola smiled and turned to look at Sally in the back seat, before saying teasingly, "I'm looking forward to two big orders from you, Marcus—one for the official engagement and then the wedding, of course." She sighed, pleasurably. "A few months ago I thought there was nothing for me to live for, and now, quite suddenly, life is beautiful and thrilling. You're such a dependable man, Marcus, and it's so good to feel that you're not only in love with Sally, but that you like me a little too. I'm sure a younger son-inlaw would irritate me frightfully, and . . ."

"Mother, you're . . ."

But Marcus too broke in calmly. "We're not hurrying anything, Viola, but you can count on my help in every way."

"I'm sure of it. And thank you for the introduction to Captain Northwick."

"It's all that was necessary," he said with a smile. "He was sold from the moment you met."

At Las Viñas, Sally went ahead while Marcus put a helping hand to Viola's elbow. They mounted the steps, crossed the courtyard and entered the coolness of the hall. On the carved table lay an orderly pile of letters, and Sally lingered, waiting for Marcus to go through them. He gave a couple to Viola, selected another envelope, after examining the postmark, and gave it to Sally.

"From Malaga," he said, with a cool smile. "It's been readdressed from your hotel in Barcelona."

Viola looked round from halfway up the staircase. "A letter from that boy Peter?" she asked, raising a slender eyebrow. "Hadn't you better tear it up without reading it?"

"Why should I?" asked Sally. "I'm sure you wouldn't do that to a letter from one of your friends."

Viola shrugged and went on up the stairs. Sally turned to follow her, and as she did so she caught a small movement of Marcus's from the corner of her eye. She wasn't sure, but she thought he'd drawn one of the letters from the batch and fitted it into his pocket.

"Darling," said her mother, as she reached her side, "will you come into my room and unhook me? The lunch that man served us seems to have weighted my arms!"

Sally performed the small task, peeled the pale peach linen from her mother and hung up the frock. Viola had stepped out of her shoes and was reaching for eau de cologne and a tissue.

"I'm going to rest for two solid hours," she said. "After such a morning I need it." She laughed softly, helplessly. "Did you ever see such a house?" Those horrible pictures and the chairs! That refectory table in the sitting room! Now, if that table were in the dining room and there were small windsor chairs and that beastly chiffonier were replaced by a Welsh dresser . . . the man has no taste at all."

"He simply ordered things that he thought matched his income."

"But that dreadful capstan in the porch."

"It's a binnacle."

"Whatever it is, it should have been left on a ship. The cottage is just a picture of his life—a welter of ships and ugly, expensive furniture. The man hasn't really lived yet, and he must be nearly sixty."

"He's having his own idea of a good life. Isn't that what we all want?"

Viola sighed. "You're serious about those things, aren't you? You know, dear, you're not behaving like a girl in love. I know you and Marcus only became engaged so soon because he wanted our position here to be clear from the very start, but shouldn't you try to be with him more? And don't you sometimes feel you want him to slip an arm round you and even kiss you occasionally in front of others? He'd do it like a shot if you showed the smallest inclination that way."

Sally wondered, a little bleakly, how her mother would react if she were told that not a single embrace had been exchanged between Sally and Marcus Durant.

"It takes time to know a man like Marcus," she said, "but I'm sure he's not the sort to like any outward show of affection."

"Don't be silly. He was human enough to stake a claim on you within two or three weeks of meeting you, and if he's holding back it's for your sake, not his. A man of his age is bound to have had affairs, and perhaps you feel awfully young and untried. But you're a nurse, darling, and nurses know everything. If I were you . . ."

"But you're not, are you? I don't even have a little of your temperament—so I have to go about this in my own way."

"Well, it's not a very sensible way, darling. Marcus is very masculine, and if you're too embarrassed to show your feelings he'll start getting unmanageable—and I can imagine nothing more devasting than a man like Marcus who has got out of hand! As a matter of fact," she ended with soft insistence, "he's already a little impatient with you, and I can guess why. That darting into the back seat of the car and running ahead up the steps, and clutching the letter from the pianist boy . . . all those actions are typical of the way you're behaving with your own fiancé. It's quite unnatural and not like you at all."

Sally's tones hardened a little. "Getting engaged is not like me, either. Perhaps I've made a mistake."

"Don't say that!" Viola had stopped dabbing at her forehead with the stopper of the eau de cologne bottle. Her smile had gone and her blue eyes looked frightened. "Don't ever say that again, Sally. We're depending on Marcus now —he's all we have."

Sally turned to the door. Her throat felt raw, but she answered casually, "He told you that you can count on him; that's all the assurance you need. Have a nice sleep."

Sally went into her own room and stood for a moment near the foot of the bed, looking out across the balcony at the archway full of blue sky trimmed at the edges with the green tips of the trees. Then, slowly, she opened the letter from Peter Malling. But there was nothing in it to dispel the depression. He had written it on his first day in Spain, when she had been on her way from Malaga to Barcelona, and so much had happened since then that Peter himself had become cloudy and unreal.

She walked out into the balcony and sat down, leant her head back against the wall and tried to recapture some of the sweetness of her talks with Peter, the dreamy rapture of listening to the music he made. Strangley, she could only see them objectively, herself and Peter. Herself bemused by the speeding waves, luxurious idleness and the first light touch of love; and Peter, absorbed with his own emotions and opportunities and trying for all he was worth to appear sophisticated and bohemian; both of them rather pathetic viewed from the stark reality of the present.

Deliberately, she shredded the letter. Unless he heard from her he wouldn't write again; he was too selfish as well as too sensitive to risk a rebuff. In any case, he had written quickly, while still under the spell of the Mediterranean; by now it would have worn off and someone else would be listening with flattering intensity to his words and music.

A small cloud passed over the sun and she realized it was cooler. She got up and tossed the fragments of paper into the decorative white waste-box, got into flat shoes and went into the corridor. After a second's hesitation she walked quietly down the stairs and into the rather cosy little morning room. From the window, she made sure that the courtyard was empty; she could go out the front way. It was as she turned from the window that she caught sight of a piece of paper which a breeze must have wafted to the far corner, under the rather large writing desk. Automatically she crossed the room and bent to retrieve it, and almost, as she straightened, she crushed it into a ball. Then she realized that it wasn't merely a scrap accidentally torn from a newspaper; it was a cutting which had been attached to something else, for the corner was ragged where it had become detached.

She read, unthinkingly; read again and felt chilled. It was about a play which had been booked to run for six weeks in New York, and a paragraph which had been marked with a tiny red cross said: "Nadine Carmody gives a good rounded performance as the judge's naughty daughter. A pity that this play has to go on tour before she made the impact she deserves."

That was all, really. Sally turned the clipping and saw that a date and the name of the newspaper had been penned on the back of it. And instinctively she knew that it had been pinned to a letter which Marcus had read in this room only a short while ago; the letter she had seen him push into his pocket.

She slipped the cutting just under the edge of the blotter so that part of it was visible, and went through the hall to the courtyard. After staring across at the hills for a few minutes she went down into the garden and strolled. Her head was aching a little and misery seemed to have settled like a ball of lead just below the base of her throat. Though heaven knew why a few printed words should make her feel benighted. She had known of Nadine Carmody's existence and might have guessed that a few words of praise in an American newspaper would certainly find their way to Las Viñas. What she hadn't bargained for was her own sudden disquiet. Or was disquiet too mild a word? Could she possibly be . . . jealous?

No, that was absurd. Her feeling was a natural revulsion from her own situation. Nadine Carmody should have been here at Las Viñas, wearing the sapphire, getting to know Doña Inez, talking of wedding plans, and being made love to by Marcus. But Nadine had been too dazzled by her own minor success in the theatre to contemplate settling on San Palos in comparative obscurity. And events had conspired to place Sally Sheppard in Nadine's place; so there was no talk of wedding plans, no lovemaking— only an insidious growing hostility within her towards Marcus; which Sally couldn't understand.

Looked at sanely, her position was quite clear and simple. In return for being delivered from the horror of finding herself and her mother adrift in Barcelona, and the relief of finding sanctuary at Las Viñas with the promise of posts on the island, Sally was providing the old *señora* with a new and sparkling reason for living. What she had to cling to was the fact that she was doing nothing for Marcus himself. As he had pointed out, when the time came for ending the engagement it would be she who would emerge triumphant, not he. The whole thing was uncomfortable, and it spoiled any chance they might have had of becoming normal and tranquil friends, but there was no doubt of its beneficial effect upon Doña Inez. So what had Sally Sheppard to grouse about?

Was she falling a little for Marcus? Perhaps, but it was only because she had nothing to do. And anyway, she felt more at peace with boys like Peter or men like Carlos Suarez. Marcus made her too aware of herself and her youth, and there was nothing to bind them. The most astonishing thing was other people's acceptance of the engagement.

Sally lay down under her favorite tree and dozed, and presently the headache receded and her usual composure returned. She sauntered back to the house, walked carelessly into the morning room and noticed that the newspaper clipping had gone. Perhaps he would sleep with it under his pillow tonight. She hoped it would give him night-mares.

*   *   *

It was not till next morning that Sally met the new house-guest, Josef Carvallo. He had arrived during the previous evening and gone straight to his room, and though mention had been made of him at dinner, there seemed to be no question of asking him to join the guests. When Sally saw him after breakfast next morning, she knew why. Josef, with a heavy white bandage about his head and a thick dressing gown belted about his slim frame, looked quite ill. He sat outdoors with a glass of orange juice on the table beside him, and talked to Marcus, who appeared to have been up for hours. Sally had been going to wave vaguely to them and go down the steps, but Marcus called her and came to meet her, took her arm and led her towards Josef Carvallo. Before an introduction could be made Josef said breezily,

"*Buenos dias, señorita!* You are well this morning?" He gave Marcus a broad wink. "But you are lucky, Marcus. She is fresh as a rose. And I am eternally in her debt for what she has done for me. Even one more day in that nursing home would have sent me mad. Many thanks, *señorita.*"

"I did nothing for you, nothing at all," she stated quickly.

Marcus slanted a keen glance from one to the other. "Have you two met?"

She nodded. "Yes, when I toured with Carlos. Señor Carvallo asked me to tell you about his plight, but I didn't have to. You'd already heard."

"Why didn't you say you'd met Josef?"

Josef laughed. "He is not so sure of himself as he used to be—this Marcus. It seems that also he is not sure of you, *señorita!* Yet look at me. In this condition am I attractive to any woman, let alone to one as pretty as you?"

With a sardonic smile Marcus said, "You're well aware

75

of your chief attraction at the moment—that bandage is worth more than gold. Keep it, if you want to, but don't go in to see Doña Inez till you're decently dressed and the bandage is discarded."

"And you promise that we shall have no serious discussions till I am quite recovered?"

"Yes, but I'll take Carlos' word for your condition, not yours."

Josef shrugged dejectedly. "You are a hard man, Marcus. One would have thought that being in love would have softened you—that you would have declared yourself willing to forget the past and begin again with me. *Señorita*, will you not plead with him for me?"

"Don't you already have what you wanted?" she asked lightly. "You're here at Las Viñas, and Marcus has said he'll postpone discussions—whatever that may mean—till you're quite fit. What more is there?"

"With Josef," said Marcus, "there's always more. He probably has a new scheme for getting rich quick."

"It is an old scheme, and it would not make me rich— only satisfied."

"Really?" In spite of Marcus's cynical presence, Sally was interested. "What is it?"

"Ceramics," was the reply. "I wish to start my own small factory on San Palos."

"Oh." She looked uncertainly at Marcus, saw that he was unimpressed. "Would it make much money?"

"No, but it would take a good deal of staying power," Marcus commented.

"What sort of ceramics?" she asked Josef.

"Tiles, vases, ornaments, even brooches and earrings."

"But isn't the market overloaded with that kind of thing?"

"Not with *my* designs," Josef said, spreading his hands. "Even Marcus will admit I am an original artist in ceramics."

"Oh, sure," said Marcus dismissively. "But you're no business man. You'd better go in and lie down till Carlos comes. Sally and I are going to take a drive."

"Are we?" she said. "Where are we going?"

"You'll see. So long, Josef—keep the headgear clean."

The younger man gave another pathetic little shrug that belied the twinkle in his eye. "You two have obviously not exchanged rings in the del Moscado tradition, so one may assume you are not officially engaged. If I were not under your roof, Marcus, I would try to charm your Sally away from you!"

"Why let my hospitality stop you?" said Marcus dryly. "See you later."

Sally waved a hand to Josef and descended the curving stone staircase with Marcus. It was a brilliant morning and hardly any of her uncertainties had yet seeped back into her consciousness. She felt free and tenuously happy. Here she was, with a tall, fine-looking man at her side and an atmosphere that promised mild excitement all about her. What more could she want?

They drove out on to the road, but instead of turning right, towards Naval Town, he took the left and they climbed a long hill from which, looking back, Sally could see the sloping acres of Las Viñas, with the old house roughly central among the trees.

"Did you live here as a boy?" she asked him.

"I didn't leave the island at all till I was nine. I had a tutor, and he took me to school in England. For the next ten years or so I flew home only for holidays, and then my father died and I had to take over here."

"And since then there's been only you and Doña Inez at Las Viñas?"

He nodded. "She was active until a couple of years ago, and we entertained on a big scale. There were always house-guests from Majorca or Spain, and when celebrities came cruising through the Mediterranean they invariably put in at San Palos and my grandmother made them an excuse for a function of some sort. We had a whole film company here once."

"What did she make of them?"

He gave her a smile and turned his attention back to the winding road. "She loved them. She always used to say that though she never left the island she was cosmopolitan —she brought the world here. At one time she used to make the headlines, even in England; at some time or other she's been hostess to every notability who's come this way."

"She looks it," said Sally. "She's a vital person, even now. What does Carlos really thing about her health?"

His smile faded. "He thinks she'll live for as long as she's determined to do so. He put it very bluntly—want to hear it?"

Sally wasn't sure, but she had to say, "Of course. I have quite a personal feeling about Doña Inez."

"Well, Carlos said it's up to me. Doña Inez is determined to see me married; after that, the coming of great-grandchildren and other milestones would keep her going till the old heart finally gave out. She's fond of Carlos and other nephews, she even has a soft corner for Josef Carvallo, but all her hopes for Las Viñas and the future are centred in me. It's natural, but a bit restricting. She's been my whole family for a long time and I'd do anything to make her happy."

"Except . . . marry?"

"I was even prepared to do that." His smile came back and he looked at her mockingly. "Pity you're not six or seven years older; we might make a go of it."

She averted her head slightly. "Do you believe that marriage can be a lukewarm arrangement between two people?"

"Not at all. Marriage has to be a partnership, and a pretty warm-blooded one at that. What I *don't* believe in is the love match."

She sent him a quick glance and saw that his expression was tolerant except for a faint line of bitterness at his mouth. "If that's how you feel," she said evenly, "you'd better start casting round for that Spanish woman. They're warm-blooded, I believe, and very willing to make a marriage of convenience."

"Certainly seems the sensible thing to do," he agreed laconically. "It would solve my problems." There was

78

a pause, and then he asked, "Is it getting you down—the situation?"

"I can bear it," she said coolly.

"Supposing things were to get stickier?"

"How could they?"

A shrug. "You proved yesterday when you went out with Carlos that I can't keep you imprisoned at the house for weeks on end. But the more you circulate the more tricky the situation is likely to become."

She said hesitantly, "Marcus, couldn't you let me work as a nurse at the hospital? That would cut out much of the social life, and I'd promise never to say one word about . . . about you and me."

His dark eyes appraised her briefly. "I'd trust you a long way, Sally, but for the present I can't let you work. To the islanders you've become part of the del Moscado family, someone they rather look up to. The people are simple, and it would outrage something deep inside them if you took your place with the nurses in the new section of the nursing home. Even the British people here would think it strange."

In low tones she said, "They'll regard it as even more peculiar if I start nursing here after I've broken with you. Or maybe you think it will prove to others that I'm not quite up to the standard of Las Viñas?"

"That's not a bit smart," he said sharply. "At this stage one can't see into the future, anyway. One of the reasons for this drive is that I want us to understand each other a little better, so that you can enjoy everything."

"I think you do understand *me*."

"Not quite." He had slowed the car so that they were cruising along beside a small flowering orchard. "I hadn't really much option other than to let the situation develop, but I'd certainly have opposed it in some way if I hadn't thought you were the kind of girl who'd get some sort of kick out of it. Back on the ship, among those young people, you were gay and spirited, game for anything. I noticed you went quiet when I was about, but I took it to be uncertainty, because you didn't know me. You do know me now, though."

"By no means thoroughly."

"Enough to have confidence in me, anyway," he said abruptly.

"I do have confidence in you, and I've no false feelings about staying at Las Viñas while we're supposed to be . . . engaged. Luckily I don't *feel* engaged, so when people congratulate me or link us in some way it's like listening to part of a play."

"That's interesting. What am I in this play—the villain who forced you into a liaison? Are you hoping a hero will come to the rescue?"

She laughed. "It's not as unreal as all that. I suppose I could rescue myself if it became necessary. Where are we going?"

"You want a change of topic? Very well—we're going up towards the perfume distillery. When we get past these olives and figs you'll see the lilac."

"Is it in bloom?"

"It's just coming out. It'll be at its best in about a week."

"And then the trees are cleared?"

"Yes, but the complete picking seems to force a second flowering in some of the trees; it's not so profuse and the blossoms aren't as good as the first, but it's quite a sight." He swung the car round a wide bend and gestured. "Look. Ever see anything like that in England?"

The fruit orchards of Kent and Worcester might be comparable, Sally thought, but they hadn't the miraculous coloring of the San Palos lilac. It wasn't true lilac color but much paler, and when the sprays were full-blown the effect would be a glorious expanse of pastel mauve. There seemed to be miles of those crowded trees with their new green leaves and masses of bloom, with here and there a farm cottage in its patch of vegetables and fruit trees.

"Is this run in farms like the vines?" she asked.

"Yes, but the farms are bigger. We buy up and distil, and the essence goes to a perfume factory in France. This is the only acreage of this particular variety of lilac in the world. You'll see garden specimens throughout the Mediterranean, but we're the only commercial growers. And guess who started the industry here!"

"The Englishman who married your grandmother?"

"He did it to please her, and was always rather ashamed of the lilacs. As I remember him, he invariably smelled belligerently of tweed and horses; we had no cars on the island in those days."

"I'm sure he was a darling."

"He was all right," Marcus conceded tolerantly. "He certainly showed some good sense when he married Inez del Moscado."

She said musingly, "It's nearly seventy years ago, isn't it? Isn't it a pity one can't look back and see things exactly as they were? Was he handsome?"

"As a young man? Fairly, I think. He'd been a soldier and was recuperating in his yacht after a wound. He was hurt again when the yacht hit the rocks, and he was carried up to Las Viñas—a matter of a mile and a half—on a grass stretcher-bed. It was inevitable that the big brown-haired soldier laid low by wounds should fall in love with the dark young beauty who helped to nurse him."

She said, with a sigh. "The truly romantic things seem always to have happened in the past, don't they? If a yacht foundered today the crew would be whipped into the hospital, mended in no time and sent on their way."

"The Casa de Curacion existed then, of course, but there was just one very old physician on the island, so the place only took in people who couldn't be nursed at home—generally the very old or incurably sick. They had only a dozen beds, anyway. Now they have more than sixty." He paused. "Talking of romance—it's all a matter of outlook. There's still pathos in a white bandage and colorless cheeks; you'll admit that?"

She smiled. "You're very hard on your cousin Josef. He doesn't look at all well."

"Did he tell you he was my cousin?" he asked at once.

"You yourself said he was a connection of some sort."

"A very distant one," said Marcus. "He's no more my cousin that you are."

"Oh, I naturally thought, as you took charge . . ."

"I did that for Doña Inez," he said. "For her sake I've tried to get Josef to take a job in Spain. But the minute you speak of work he knows of some easier way to get money."

"That's not quite fair. Some people find life much more difficult than others, and that's particularly true of the creative type. Is he really an artist in ceramics?"

"Yes, he's pretty good."

"You sound grudging. If he's good, why can't you help him to get the factory he wants?"

"Because I'd probably be left with it on my hands after a year, or less. You don't know Josef at all. I know him too well."

"Well, can't you help him to get started in the same thing somewhere else? I mean, couldn't he become a partner to someone who's already established? Then if the time came when he wanted to back out . . ."

"I wouldn't wish Josef on to anyone. When it suits him he can be strong-minded and independent, but you never know quite what he's up to. I haven't seen him for two years, but I know he's been trying to get some cash, through Katarina." He stopped speaking, turned into a lilac-bordered lane and then added, "Josef upset a very sweet San Palos girl when she was on the point of marrying someone else. The engagement was ended, but after Josef had been absent for some time we all thought the young couple might come together again. His return just now may set the thing back a couple of years. He's a damned nuisance."

"He's not fit," Sally said. "Hasn't he a home somewhere?"

"No." Marcus spoke dismissively, in hard tones. "Be careful what you say to him. If he should suspect our engagement we're finished . . . and so is Doña Inez."

Sally would have liked to defend the dark young man with the pale face and black curly hair above the white

82

bandage. But they were approaching a long low house which was set in a small formal garden among the lilacs, and she could see a middle-aged man and woman rising from their chairs on the lawn and coming to the drive, to greet them.

Marcus bowed over the woman's hand, shook that of the man. "Don Pedro and Doña Isabel . . . this is Miss Sheppard. Señor and Señora Suarez," he said to Sally. "Carlos's brother and sister-in-law."

They were also Marcus's relations, presumably, but perhaps because they were in their fifties he spoke to them distantly and politely. Don Pedro, he explained, managed the perfume distillery.

The woman, dark-skinned, wearing black with a touch of white and an oramental comb in her coiled grey-black hair, smiled agreeably at Sally and took both her hands. Her English was guttural and abominable, but that rather endeared her to Sally.

"So you are zees *novia* of v'ich ve'ear. Ve 'ave vondered ven Marcus bring you to see us, and den, soddenly, 'e say zis morning you vill com'. So 'appy ve are to meed you, *señorita!*"

Her husband spoke as Carlos did, in good English heavily accented. Obviously they had been prepared for this visit, for no sooner were the four of them seated under a wide magnolia tree than an oldish maid who was bad on her feet wheeled out a wrought-iron trolley loaded with coffee and chocolate and fancy cakes. Sally answered their questions. Oh, yes, she liked San Palos very much, though she hadn't yet seen much of the coast. The nursing home? Dr. Suarez had taken her there yesterday. No, she had never before seen this variety of lilac; the flowers looked enormous and the scent, even before they were full-blown, was heavenly.

"The essence," Señor Suarez assured her, "is not heavenly at all. It is too concentrated. From each kilo of flowers we extract only two or three drops, so that an ounce of the essence is worth much money. We will ask you, *señorita*, to honor us this year at the Lilac Fiesta—to be our queen, if Marcus will permit it."

"Why not?" said Marcus, with an amused smile. "She'll be the fairest queen you've ever had."

"But I don't belong here," Sally said hastily. "Please choose someone else!"

"You do not understand," the Spaniard murmured reassuringly. "Our Lilac Fiesta is not like the Mardi Gras or the Battle of Flowers. The pickers work unceasingly, day and night, for perhaps two weeks. When the final batch is in the presses the pickers collect their pay—and what is the good of money if there is no way of spending it soon? So for two days they rest and prepare. In the field near the distillery they erect sideshows and cafés, a platform for their band, and a throne of lilacs for the queen, who must be gowned in white with sprays of lilac."

"Mos' bewdiful," crooned his wife. "You vill look sharming!"

"I really couldn't," said Sally desperately. "Marcus . . ."

But he was no help at all. "Why not give the folk a treat?" he said reasoningly. "You won't have to do a thing except sit in your bower and smile for about half an hour. After that, you dance a couple of times and then disappear."

"But isn't the whole affair an island celebration? Isn't it more fair to have one of the local girls as queen? And in any case, in three weeks' time I'll . . ." She broke off, dry-lipped.

Marcus said suavely, "Don Pedro, as the head of the business, has invited you, and you can accept provisionally. He doesn't expect more than that at the moment."

"Of course nod," came throatily from the gracious Doña Isabel. "Vill you some more shocolate like?"

Sticky from the moments of apprehension, Sally politely declined, and to her relief Marcus said they must go. But the ordeal wasn't over yet. Señora Suarez rang the bell on the trolley and spoke swiftly in Spanish to the woman who had hobbled out to answer it. Sally caught a swift glance of warning from Marcus, and was glad, in the next few minutes, that she hadn't missed it.

For the servant went off and returned carrying a six-inch silk-covered square box which Señora Suarez took from her.

With great decorum, holding the box in both hands, the Spanish woman presented it to Sally.

"Please to receive this, vith our vishes from the 'eart. My 'usband will explain."

Señor Suarez bowed, and spoke quietly with a smile. "Marcus understands these customs of ours, but as an engagement happens only once in a man's lifetime he will not, perhaps, be fully aware of what this betrothal means to us, his family."

"It still isn't official, you know," Sally said desperately. "Couldn't you please . . ." Marcus's hand closing tightly about her elbow magically cut off the flow.

The *señor* shrugged comprehendingly. "This gift is not for the engagement. It is for the woman who has come into our family—a personal gift from my wife to you. Please open the box."

With quivering fingers Sally lifted the lid. Inside the box, separated by folds of fine white velvet, lay two exquisite crystal perfume containers; one was a bottle with a glass stopper and the other was spherical with a gold spray cap. The latter held a champagne-colored liquid.

"San Palos lilac," said Don Pedro. "It was blended in Paris."

Somehow Sally kept a hold on the box and managed to stammer her thanks. The two were benign and understanding, and touchingly pleased that their gift should make such an impression on Marcus's fiancée. Perhaps for safety's sake, Marcus took charge of the precious box before he added his thanks to Sally's and put her into the car.

Sally said her goodbyes and waved her hand, felt the trembling leave her limbs and vexation fill her throat like angry tears. They were back on the road when she eventually trusted herself to speak.

"That's the ninth gift! Why do you let these people keep giving me things? Those presents from guests the other night and the set of leather-bound books from Carlos. They're not mine and I don't want them!"

"Just an old del Moscado custom," he said with infuriating calm. "I can't get worked up about a few scent sprays and books and trinkets. There's too much else involved."

"Well, why in the world do they have to anticipate the official engagement?" she choked. "I can't stand it!"

"Oh, come, you're losing your sense of proportion. They're my relatives and the gifts are the customary tokens. Put them away and forget them."

"What about this beastly *fiesta*?" she returned crossly. "I'm darned if I'll be their lilac queen!"

"But just imagine," he said mockingly. "A white gown sprayed with lilac and the little flowerets forming a crown on your hair. Mos' bewdiful. You vill look sharming!"

Suddenly, because in spite of being angry she was amused by his atrocious mimicry, she laughed aloud. He slipped his arm round her shoulder and squeezed it, and for a startled moment she looked up. As she did so her nose brushed his chin and he turned a light kiss upon her cheek. She drew a quick breath and got back into her corner.

"That's not in the bargain," she said in controlled tones. "Don't do it again."

"Why?" with satire. "Are you afraid you might want to kiss me back?"

"No, it's nothing like that. I've agreed to stand in for Nadine Carmody, but only up to a point. And that point doesn't include kisses, matey or otherwise."

Abruptly, he withdrew his arm and let his foot go down hard upon the accelerator. They shot forward. Not another word or look was exchanged between them, but when they reached Las Viñas she saw the bitterness lining one corner of his mouth, and heard cynicism in his voice as he said, in the hall,

"You're quite attractive, damn you. But I sure picked a fledgling in you, didn't I? Run along."

She went up the staircase to her room, carrying the pink silk box as if it were a bomb. But inside the room she stood rooted, staring at the confusion on the writing table, the half-open drawers.

CHAPTER FIVE

IT was not a wanton confusion; Sally saw that at once. Rather it was as though the person who had been looking for something had had little time in which to do it; had she been absent another ten minutes Sally might never have known that her room had been searched.

She moved forward and placed her box on the dressing table, where things had merely been pushed aside to clear a space for operations. But what operations? What had they hoped to find here? More important, what had they *found*?

Quickly, her fingers uncertain, Sally went through her belongings. Lingerie had been hunted through and left lumpy, the wardrobe doors were ajar, the small valise she kept in there had been lifted out and opened. It was the contents of the valise which were scattered on the writing table; letters, her passport, birth certificate, bank book and a few odd papers relating to St. Alun's. The strange thing was that not a single item seemed to be missing. What in the world had they wanted? Had they heard the car returning, perhaps seen it from the balcony, and had to slip away before completing their search? If so, they might try it again.

She shivered in the midday warmth, went across to the balcony and looked down on to the only part of the courtyard which was visible—a length of the wall and the top of the steps. Josef, in a white shirt and dark trousers, stood there, looking worn and disconsolate. He had apparently called for a drink, for as Sally watched, Katarina brought him a glass and he thanked her for it. They spoke for a minute, then Katarina touched his hand with the familiarity of an old retainer and went away.

Sally backed into her room, passed a hand over her forehead. She ought to report this upheaval in her room to Marcus, wouldn't have hesitated but for those last minutes in the car. Better to think it over a little, anyway.

As she tidied the desk and dressing table Sally's mind did its utmost to focus on the seemingly senseless rootling among her possessions. One of the servants? It was most unlikely; they'd expect her to tell Marcus and be terrified of the consequences. Josef Carvallo? Poor Josef; according to Carlos his wound was deep and might throb for days when he moved his head quickly. He was certainly in no condition to make a lightning trip upstairs and a hurried search. And what would he be looking for? What would *anyone* expect to find in Sally Sheppard's room?

There came a rap at the door and she called, "Come in."

But Katarina remained in the opened doorway. "Doña Inez says she has missed your visit with Don Marcus this morning. Don Marcus is now with guests who have been waiting for him, and the *señora* says she will see him later. But you will come now, *señorita?*"

"Alone?" asked Sally, perturbed. She hadn't yet seen the old lady alone.

"It is what she asks," stated the woman with a shrug. Her dark eyes were blank, but the mole near the left corner of her brown lips twitched as she added, "Do not forget the ring you always wear for Doña Inez. If it is absent she will notice."

Sally slid the ring on to her finger, and as she straightened she looked at Katarina, the faithful servant who fiercely loved the old *señora* and Marcus. Clearly, she said, "I've had a most disturbing experience, Katarina. When I came in fifteen minutes ago this room was almost a shambles. Someone had been searching through my things."

Katarina looked startled. *"Dios!* Is that true? How could it be so? Up here there has only been the *señora* and myself and Maria, who cleans the rooms. I have been with Doña Inez all the morning until a few minutes ago, when I made a tisane for her and gave some to Josef, who has been complaining of pain in his head. I cannot be completely sure that no one has come to this side of the house, but it is most unlikely."

"Well, *someone* did it."

"Then you must tell Don Marcus at once. Something was stolen?"

"No, nothing. I don't want to upset the household, so I won't tell anyone unless it happens again. Are you certain there's been no one up here?"

"I have been all the time with the *señora*—how can I be certain? All I can say is that there have been only four servants, Doña Inez and Señora Sheppard in the house—except the guests who arrived half an hour ago and were greeted by the *señora* your mother."

"Who are they?"

"Captain Northwick, Mr. McCartney of the hotel, and the Commander of Naval Bay, with his wife."

"Mr. McCartney? Has he been here as a guest before?"

"A few times." Katarina's shrug indicated her opinion of the hotel proprietor. "There is some business deal, I think."

"Would Mr. McCartney be able to get up here?"

"I think not. Why should he search your room? Why should *anyone* search your room?"

"I wish I knew the answer to that. If I discover it was a maid," she said distinctly, "I'll get her sacked."

"It was no maid," returned Katarina. "They are much too happy, all of them, to have you here as the fiancée of Don Marcus; they would not risk your displeasure in any way. You would be well advised to tell Don Marcus. He will get to the root of it. Will you come now? The *señora* takes her luncheon at twelve-thirty, and it is nearly that time."

Sally slanted a hurried glance at herself in the dressing-table mirror as she passed it to go from the room. Luckily she didn't look as flustered as she felt. She followed Katarina along the corridor, past the landing and on into the far room. Alone, she entered it.

Doña Inez, looking smaller than ever, was lying back among her pillows. Today her bed-jacket was a delicate pink which made the skin of her cheeks look thinner and paler; her eyes were dark, but not quite so fiery as usual, though they followed Sally's movements with birdlike keenness.

Her voice sounded a little hoarse this morning. "Come and sit, my dear. For the first time we are alone, no?"

Sally took the chair beside the bed, smiled gently. "It's against the rules, I believe."

"The rules of Marcus, yes. Early this morning he told me you two would come to me for tea this afternoon. But I knew you had returned and that he would be with the guests, so I told Katarina to see if you were in your room. It is time we had a talk. When Marcus is here you say nothing."

"Is it good for you to talk today, *señora?*"

"It is good," she answered firmly. "We will not discuss, only chat. Tell me where you and Marcus have been this morning."

This was easier than Sally had anticipated; she relaxed slightly. "We visited Don Pedro and Señora Suarez."

"Ah, I like Pedro, and my niece Isabel is a good woman, even though she has the speech of a *campesina.* You enjoyed the visit?"

"Very much, and I thought the lilacs enchanting."

"Soon they will be unbearably beautiful, and then they will vanish." The gnarled, bony fingers of her hands became hooked together like claws. "And Marcus—do you find him also enchanting?"

"Not exactly. He's too down-to-earth for that."

"But no. One's companion in love *should* be enchanting." She paused, rested her gimlet glance once more upon the fair young face. "There are perhaps things about this being in love that you do not understand. When you are in here with Marcus I can feel it. He is a man of strong reactions and you are young and inexperienced. Does it worry you that you do not make him happy?"

Alarm sent a chill through Sally. For a second she was on the verge of a vehement disclaimer, but the next moment it came to her that this was an opportunity she might use, very carefully.

"You feel Marcus is not happy, *señora?*" she asked quietly.

"I have always felt his moods. We have always been very close, Marcus and I. Over the years our more intimate contacts have necessarily been fewer. He is a man, with a

90

man's appetites and needs, and I am only an old woman who cares more for him than for anyone else, but who knows nothing of his world outside San Palos. Since he has returned with you he has not been himself. He is too sauve, and his good humor does not go deep. Underneath, his mood is dark."

And good reason for it, Sally thought bleakly. He'd been turned down by the woman he had chosen; he'd shown intolerance, really, but to his autocratic mind it didn't look that way. The way he saw it, a few months of acting in America had taken his place in the heart of Nadine Carmody.

"That's something I can't explain, I'm afraid," she said. "I'm not at all sure what it takes to make Marcus happy."

"In that, he is no different from other men. He needs your love and dependence on him. There are things about him that you naturally do not know, but if you love him well you will learn them. Do you know how I really feel about Marcus?"

"Yes, I think so," said Sally, very carefully. "He's . . . he's everything."

"I did not mean my love for him. There is the other thing —his love for me. Always, throughout the years, he has come back to *madrecita*. Sometimes there have been many months, and once, while he was at university, he stayed away for two years. But then a day came when he walked up the steps and I was there in the courtyard to greet him. He has never been disappointed in me because always I have been here, waiting. Many times he has said, very English, 'You are a lightweight anchor, old lady, but the strongest in the world.' Do you comprehend what I am saying?"

"Yes," said Sally thinly. "I believe I understand very well."

"Then you will tell me . . . plainly, so that I may be sure."

Sally resisted an urge to moisten her lips. She looked at the frail little woman, managed a smile and replied, "It comes back to something you've said yourself, to Marcus; you want him to marry soon. You want to be sure he'll always have the strong anchor, someone he loves and needs."

"Good."

Apparently, having reached that point, Doña Inez had decided she needed respite. She closed her eyes, and Sally hoped rather desperately that she would either slip into a doze or wave her away. The minutes passed. The scent of roses drifted up from the climbers on the balustrade and the dainty gold clock on the mantelpiece sent its merry little ticking across the room. Sally shifted, and at once the old *señora* opened her lively dark eyes.

"You think I am old-fashioned?" she demanded. "You think it is out of date that one should wish a fine old estate to be carried on long after one is dead, by one's own family?" She gave Sally no time to answer. "The good, solid things are never old-fashioned, but unfortunately one's years are limited. I do not doubt that Marcus will always give himself to Las Viñas, but I am foolish enough to want to see some way into the future. Tell me, *señorita,* why do you hold back from the official betrothal?"

Sally felt as if she had received a blow in the solar plexus. She swallowed and heard an odd singing noise in her ears. Crazily, she had thought she might get a little of her own way with this small, ancient volcano, but what a hope! All the *señora's* strength had become concentrated in those sharp wits which circled warily round the one thing that mattered in her universe.

Sally drew an audible breath. "I've been here such a short time, *señora.* Perhaps you are expecting too much."

"You have known Marcus for much longer. He has proposed to you and told you he loves you. You have consented to marry him and, knowing Marcus, I cannot believe he has not urged that you quickly make the engagement official and arrange the wedding. Therefore it is logical to conclude that it is you who are reluctant, no?"

Sally's fingers were gouging holes in her palms. Dare she reply to this truthfully, dare she try to . . . ? She suddenly saw the *señora's* face very clearly. There was a dew of perspiration on the lined white forehead and a terrible anxiety in the black eyes; the thin knobbly hands had parted from each other and were clutching the crisp embroidered foldover of the sheet.

Swiftly Sally leaned forward and stroked the hand nearest her. In unsteady, smiling tones she said, "You must give me time, Doña Inez. I have no Spanish blood, only an ordinary English temperament. I love San Palos, and Las Viñas is the most beautiful place I've ever seen, but everything is very new to me and I have to feel my way. Couldn't you give me a few weeks to get thoroughly acclimatized? By then I'll know more about myself . . . and Marcus."

"You must know already how you feel for him."

"Yes, said Sally with fatalistic calm. "I do know."

"Then there is no need for so much delay. But you are sweet and perhaps shy. We will say no more for the present."

"You should rest for ten minutes or you won't enjoy your lunch."

"Yes, you are right. You were a good nurse, no?"

"I wanted to be a good one."

"You are not like your mother. She is nervous with me, like a pretty animal under the eye of an eagle. She has looks, but no mental stamina."

A shrewd valuation which Sally did not contradict; the old *señora* might have been amused, but she wouldn't have been flattered had she known Viola's opinion of her. Sally stood up, and as she did so Doña Inez lifted one cheek, as she always did to Marcus. Sally bent and touched her lips to it, and she felt the papery fingers touch her cheek.

"Do not be afraid of life," said the tired old voice softly. "The courage will be there when you need it. I will expect you with Marcus at four. *Adios.*"

Sally answered her and got out of the room. By the time she reached her own bedroom she had control of her limbs, but there was still a tightness in her chest and a burning sensation behind her eyes. Without pausing to think, she stripped and had a cool bath and put on a black skirt and a gay blouse. Resolutely, she made up, stepped into black shoes and went downstairs. For the rest of the day, she told herself firmly, she would stick close to her mother. There

93

was one blessedly dependable fact about Viola Sheppard; nothing heartshaking ever happened while she was within hearing.

*   *   *

For several days life was soothingly quiet for Sally. Viola was mildly excited about the quick progress in the preparation of her flower department and the fact that Captain Northwick had decided to lease a tiny property adjoining the store which belonged to McCartney. This could eventually be turned into a gardening and pottery department of which Viola would have charge.

"The pretty side of the garden," she explained to Sally, "and many more indoor plants. There'll be a selection of flower holders and plant pots, hanging baskets and other decorative oddments. It would be part florist's and part gift shop. And what do you think the Captain suggested—that we call it Violette! Touching, isn't it?"

Sally smiled wonderingly. It was amazing how light-hearted Viola had become. She seemed to be years removed from England, in perfect health and full of enthusiasm and the will to make the new venture successful. She saw nothing but her own rosy present and future, and if she ever thought about Sally it was with pride in her own accomplishment. For obviously without Viola Sally would never have had a look-in with Marcus.

For a day or two Sally helped her mother plan her counter and its arty-crafty backdrop, and when she was no longer needed inside the small modern department store she strolled about Naval Town or walked on the beach beyond the buildings. Once she met Carlos and again visited the nursing home with him. He was calm and kind, told her about his hospital days in Madrid, and of the difficulties of getting Spanish parents to allow their daughters to train as nurses. Even here on San Palos, he pointed out, a girl seldom saw her fiancé alone. When a couple sat on a bench facing the sea you could be sure the whole family were crowded on the very next bench, watching the courtship's progress with grim fondness.

It was not till Carlos drew the stitches from Josef's wound and left Sally to cover it with a dressing that the young man became a little difficult. On that particular morning Josef had remained in his bedroom, writing letters, and that was where Carlos had seen him. The doctor had snipped off the large dressing which had replaced the bandage, drawn out the threads and dabbed iodine on the thread wounds. Sally had stood by, receiving the discarded dressing and handing the cottonwool and iodine.

Carlos had said, "There are dressings in the bathroom next door, Sally. I put them there myself some weeks ago. Find one to cover this, will you? It needs some protection till the hair grows."

Sally had gone off to find the box of dressings and had returned to meet Carlos as he left the bedroom. The doctor had given her his quiet cordial smile. "I will leave him with you now. He needs me no longer."

She nodded and smiled, re-entered the bedroom to find Josef still seated where they had left him. He was half turned from the writing table, his head on one side, awaiting attention. With her eye, Sally measured the long regular wound which stretched back from the top of the right ear. She selected an adhesive dressing.

"Are you sure this happened in a brawl at the hotel?" she asked. "I've been told there's no crime on San Palos, so why should someone suddenly start on you?"

He shrugged deeply, his face was very close as he looked up at her. "I was unlucky. Perhaps they were seamen who had had too much to drink. It was before I entered the hotel—just outside in the dark."

"But it's straight—like a knife wound."

He agreed. "Carlos says it must have been a knife. I was so surprised that I saw nothing. I fought . . . and then was unconscious." He laughed ruefully. "I had been waiting a long time for that drink at the hotel, and I was robbed of it." A pause. "But perhaps in a way I was fortunate. You are sorry for me."

Sally pressed down the edges of the dressing and stood back. "When I first saw you, perhaps, but not now. You're looking much better. I daresay Marcus will let you go in to see Doña Inez this afternoon or tomorrow."

"Ah, yes, the old one. She does not even know I am here. Is she well?"

"Fairly. She gets up each day for an hour and walks about the bedroom."

"This attack of hers—it has not impaired her in any way?"

"I don't think so. We take great care not to worry her, though."

"She still has control of her own affairs?"

"I don't know. Why do you ask a thing like that?"

He threw out his hands theatrically, gave a nonchalant laugh which showed a quick gleam of white teeth. "Because I am broke, and very much in earnest about starting a ceramics business here on the island. My only friends at Las Viñas are Doña Inez and Katarina. Marcus tolerates me, that is all. You have chosen a peculiar man for your husband, *querida*."

Sally ignored the *querida*. By the sudden laughing glitter in his eyes she knew he had slipped it in deliberately, to find out whether she knew the Spanish equivalent for "darling." Purposefully, she snapped shut the box of dressings.

"That's my business, isn't it?"

"One would think so, but I have doubts. Marcus is not a man to fall in love."

Sally should have left him then, with a patronizing smile, but there was a little raw place in her heart which might grow more painful if she didn't do something to heal it now. Besides, she was growing tired of being treated gently by people like Carlos. Josef's approach wasn't circumspect, but it was enlivening.

"So you think I'm one of your sort," she said. "You've decided I'm after money and a position?"

"Not so cold-blooded, please," he begged cheerfully. "For a woman, a certain position in any community has glamor. And money . . . is not that what we all want? If I had only a thousand of your English pounds I would rent

96

a cottage and erect a small mill. We have almost everything here for the manufacture of ceramics—a large patch of clay and an infinity of sand and rock. My designs are after the Moorish style and it would be easy to find a market for them. But because the idea is mine, Marcus will have none of it. He is cynical and unbelieving."

"Isn't that your own fault?"

"Partly. But perhaps I will do this thing in spite of him. It is my wish to live here on San Palos, independently of Marcus, as soon as it can be arranged."

"Have you discussed it with him?"

"Marcus does not discuss, *señorita*. He makes statements." The dark eyes laughed at her again. "I am sure he did not propose to you. It is far more likely that he watched you for a while in England and then, one evening, he told you that you must come to Las Viñas decorously, with your mother, and if you fitted into the scene he would marry you." After a mildly electric pause he added, "I am sure you have never deluded yourself about Marcus. You are no more in love with him than he is with you."

Sally managed a quick reply in a light tone. "You're hardly equipped to analyse other people, Josef. If you're really so keen to get a small factory, why not talk to the business men in Naval Town—Captain Northwick, or even Mr. McCartney? They might help you."

Josef's full lips pulled slightly, making his smile unpleasant. "I hate business men, and I want this creation to be my own. No interference, no directions from people who know nothing about ceramics, no poking of the long business man's nose into my methods and accounts."

"You'll have to convince Marcus, then, won't you? Do you hate him as well as resenting him?"

With a quick change of expression Josef shrugged this off. "I cannot like him . . . it has been no more than that, till now." Still seated, with both arms about the back of his chair, he regarded her with disturbing seriousness. His voice, rounded and alien, seemed almost to throb. "At times I have envied Marcus this house and the estate, his relationship with Doña Inez. But possessions are restricting and

I have always coveted freedom . . . till the last year or two. Now I find myself more frustated and jealous than I thought possible. He has you."

The final word hung on the air between them for fully thirty seconds before Sally was able to say, without a tremor, "That's a very nice compliment, Josef, but I suspect it's a conventional one from a Spaniard. I'm sure you don't want to make my life difficult . . ."

He jumped up and came to her. "I want to make your life beautiful," he said urgently. "You are young and very pretty, you need a man who will give you excitement and joy and more love than you can use! How can you possibly be happy here? Marcus wants only a mistress for his house, a mother for his children. His whole life is the estate of Las Viñas and that actress in London!" He caught himself up, smothered an exclamation and burst out, "I did not want to mention that, *chica*, but it has been in my mind. Do not tremble—I will tell you about it if you wish."

"You've said enough," she exclaimed, white-faced. "From now on, you can keep that sort of thing to yourself."

Again he threw out his hands in the typical eager gesture. "I am so angry with myself for saying that. There was no need for you to know. This woman—the actress—is the good friend of Marcus. In London I called at his hotel and saw them together. I did not wait to speak to him because . . ."

"Because you wondered if the information you'd accidentally picked up might be useful here on San Palos! Whom were you going to tattle to—Doña Inez?"

He drooped his head dejectedly. "You think I would do a thing like that? I did not stay to speak to Marcus because I guessed the actress was his . . . *amante*. You understand? A man who takes trouble to keep the partner of his affair so far from home . . ."

"I don't want to hear any more!"

"But I cannot bear to have hurt you. You are young, but you are full of sense. When you agreed to become the fiancée of Marcus you must have known how things would be—that he would be your husband here at Las Viñas, and the lover of someone else on his trips to England and elsewhere. I am not blind, *señorita*. No one could convince me that your engagement to Marcus was not arranged for the sake of Doña Inez and the del Moscado Durant family."

"Will you please stop it!"

His tones lowered, became soft and pitying. "I am so very sorry my thoughtless mention of this woman should hurt you. And I am very much ashamed to admit that to a degree you were right when you said that I had thought to use the information here on San Palos. At first it seemed that it might procure for me the money I need for my business; Doña Inez would have bought my silence."

"The *señora* is in precarious health—she must never hear of this," Sally flung at him. "You're just a common blackmailer."

"But no," he said, and the pain in his eyes was bewilderingly genuine. "Doña Inez would not have seen it that way. And I promise that I shall say nothing to her; she has been too ill, and you must believe that I am fond of the old one. She has done much for me."

Her breath came a little heavily. "If Marcus knew what you've been contemplating he'd have you off the island within an hour."

His smile returned. "Less than an hour," he said gaily. "But you will not tell him, *cara mia*. This foolish indiscretion of mine will remain between us. I shall say nothing to Doña Inez and you will say nothing to Marcus. It is a pact between us?"

"It has to be, doesn't it?"

"Perhaps, but please do not let it make you unhappy. I want very little in return for forgetting that I saw Marcus and his actress in London—only some support from you, your friendship."

Unbearably tightened up, she said, "What does that mean, exactly?"

"Your friendship," he repeated. "That is all."

She moved blindly towards the door. "I'll be friendly towards you as long as it suits me," she said in strained tones. "I can't think why you should try to hurt me . . ."

"Hurt you?" he cried, distressed. "I wish only to help you. You are too good for the half life you would have here. I beg of you not to make official this engagement. Some day quite soon I will be able to offer help in an acceptable form. Please believe me."

But Sally did not stay to hear more. Through a sort of miasma she forced herself out of the room, and somehow her legs carried her along a short landing to the main corridor. Then she realized she was still clutching the tin of dressings, stopped and turned, to come face to face with Marcus as he stepped out of his room.

"I've been looking for you," he began. Then, swiftly, "What's the matter? Feeling grim?"

"No. No, I'm fine. I was just going to return this to the end bathroom."

"I'll do it." He took the box and turned it in his hand. "Have you been using these?"

"Yes. Carlos asked me to dress Josef's wound."

"You've done nursing," he said, still eyeing her keenly. "You wouldn't feel faint over a thing like that."

"I don't feel faint."

"Did Josef upset you?" he probed.

"I'm perfectly all right. Why did you want me?"

"I haven't had time to go down for a bathe since we arrived. Thought you might like to try out our nearest beach with me, but if you're not up to it, just come for the ride."

"I'll go some other time, thank you, Marcus."

"Some other time won't do," he said sharply. "You're coming now."

The violet eyes became huge in the pallor of her face. "I intend to catch up on correspondence this morning. Please let me pass."

"Look here, Sally . . ."

A door opened at the end of the corridor and Katarina emerged. All Sally saw was the gaunt yellow face before she was gathered tightly within Marcus's arms.

Through the thunder of her own heartbeats she heard Marcus clip out, close to her ear, "She can see your face. Close your eyes and pretend you're not detesting every second of it!"

But Sally's eyes remained wide and staring for a further moment. She saw the minute, wrapped figure on Katarina's arm, the pause while the fierce little glance took in the scene down the corridor and the queer smile of satisfaction.

Then Sally closed her eyes tightly and whispered, *"Please take me away. I can't speak to Doña Inez. I can't!"*

He managed it so smoothly that it might have been an act he had rehearsed a dozen times. Without turning, he raised his shoulder and drew her round, so that she was almost completely hidden from the tiny woman who was taking her first few faltering steps outside her bedroom. Slowly, as though it were prearranged, he walked Sally back along the corridor to the main landing and turned with her to descend the staircase. By the time they had reached the hall his arm had dropped from her shoulder, but his hand was at her elbow, guiding her into the morning room.

Sally stood just inside the door and looked at him. Her lips were pale and felt as numb as if they had been violently kissed.

"What was all that?" she asked.

"It's part of the reason I'd decided we'd go out together this morning," he said curtly. "Every two or three days Doña Inez gets touchy about this engagement business. I took in her breakfast this morning, and she got on to the subject again—said we were not to treat her as an invalid. She kept on about unnatural behavior, the care you took not to look at me, that we don't even touch hands in her presence. She made a crack about even Spanish customs permitting endearments and other things in public. From her balcony, yesterday, she saw me go out and leave you sitting outside with your mother; for her, our parting was too casual."

"So you decided to be a little less . . . casual just now. Does it mean her health is improving?"

"I hope so." Exasperated, he shoved his hands into his pockets and took a pace or two. He stopped and looked at her, smiling faintly. "I'm beginning to hate this almost as much as you do. Try to believe that and you may not feel so badly about it all."

"Isn't there something we can do? It was rather hasty, that bit of play-acting upstairs, and maybe it wasn't very wise. When the bump comes it'll hurt her all the more."

"Then we'll have to see there's no bump, won't we?" He gazed for quite some time at the Spanish figurines which adorned a side table. "Last night I asked Carlos whether she could stand an emotional shock, and he said he doubted whether she'll ever be able to stand one if it concerns me."

She gazed at him blankly. "But . . . but what can we do about it?"

"Ever since I spoke with Carlos I've been thinking it over. I was going to have this talk with you down at the beach this morning, but events upstairs rather precipitated things. You've told me several times that you like the island and Las Viñas."

"Yes, I do."

"You thought of settling here as a nurse, so it's possible you feel you could stay here more or less indefinitely. Before I go any further, tell me something. Do you find Carlos physically attractive?"

A faint flush crept up from her neck. "No. I like him, but that's all."

"Do you find me physically *un*attractive?"

The flush became a flare of scarlet. "I refuse even to think about it. I told you the other day, when . . ."

"Yes, I remember," he said coolly. "It was just something I would have liked to know before I made my proposition. Will you marry me?"

Her head went back and she gave him a long appalled stare. "Are you . . . joking?"

"I was never more serious. We can become officially engaged right away and marry in about six months' time. In fact, we simply validate this bogus situation and make a good thing of it."

"How could you possibly think I'd agree to it?" she breathed. "You may not believe in the love match, but I do. I'd have to be madly in love and have someone madly in love with me before I'd marry!"

"Mad love," he said with sarcasm, "explodes or fizzles out quicker than any other kind. In Spain, a woman . . ."

"I'm not Spanish!"

"Very well, look at it another way," he said reasoningly. "Your mother is a thousand times happier than she was when I first met her, on the ship. She has a purpose in life, a couple of admirers and a home here at Las Viñas until she marries again. Oh, yes," as she let out an exclamation, "she'll certainly marry again; she's not complete without a husband. I think you may be sure that she intends to stay permanently on San Palos. But you, subconsciously if not consciously, had decided that the time would come, perhaps within a few weeks, when you'd have to leave the island."

"I've never thought of leaving."

"It's there, just below the surface; you even have your excuse ready—that you want to complete your training."

"What does it have to do with . . . with what you've already suggested?"

"Only this. If you left your mother here you'd be lonely and wretched. You'd have no proper home, and though you might be one of the lucky few who marry doctors, you might just as easily be one of the others who marry the first man who's willing, for a home and security. You have an appealing personality, Sally, and you have the gentle touch. I wouldn't have you buffeted about while you wait for some crazy love affair to end in marriage."

"I . . . I don't think I'm going to marry at all," she said jerkily.

His smile was almost brotherly. "Oh, yes, you are. You know, the real trouble is that you didn't know young Peter Malling for long enough. If you'd got beyond the dreamy stage with him, you'd have fallen straight into the depths when you two parted—and you wouldn't be so dogmatic about love at this moment. It would have done you the world of good."

"How can you be so . . . so nonchalant about it?" she demanded shakily. "A minute ago you called this a proposition, and that's what it is. A cold, hateful, impossible proposition! I want nothing to do with it."

Evenly, he said, "When we really understand each other there'll be nothing cold or hateful about it, I assure you. I need a wife, I'm fond of you and want to make you happy, and I don't need to point out that you're accepted and liked here. Once the difficulties of the situation have disappeared you'll feel more relaxed, and the distaste, or dislike, or whatever it is, will fade out."

She put an unsteady hand to her cheek. "To you it's all very simple. You had a fiancée in England . . ."

"Let's not discuss that."

"It's part of the whole," she said huskily. "I know why you think it's a pity I didn't have an affair with Peter. If it had ended unhappily it might have left me weak and willing. Yours was rather more than an affair, but you're a man, so your reaction was rather different. You lost the woman you wanted, so any presentable woman will do now, and if she happens to be young and tractable . . ."

"Good lord, no one could call you tractable!"

". . . so much the better," she ended the sentence, as if he had not spoken. "You can't blame me if I feel insulted!"

His posture did not alter by a fraction, but his whole body and the hawklike face became taut; his eyelids narrowed, so that the irises of his eyes looked like flashes of jet.

The odd foreign intonation came into his voice as he said, "That is a peculiar reception for the greatest compliment a man can pay a woman. You know me well enough to be sure that I'm not acting impulsively. You are also capable of weighing up the benefits to yourself. For my part, I shall be only too happy to have this situation eased and the future planned. Needless to say, my wife will always be my first consideration, in everything."

"But you won't be in love with her, because some other woman . . ."

"Others are irrelevant!" he said, at last allowing anger to become audible in his tones. "You must think it over sanely, and we'll talk again in a few days. It will help you if I go out for the rest of the day. Tomorrow morning we'll go out to the beach, perhaps—or wherever you wish. We'll see more of each other, alone. I shan't want your decision till you're quite ready to give it."

"You have my decision," she said unsteadily. "For Doña Inez I'll go along as we are for a while, but beyond that . . . nothing doing."

"Think it over," he said again. "Ask yourself what it is you really hate. Is it me, or is it a situation in which a caress becomes a stage gesture? Take your time over it. We won't discuss it again till you've thought about it."

Without another word he went from the room, and Sally was left standing as she had stood throughout the interview, only a pace or two inside the door with the back of a chair behind her, for support. She slumped back against it, with the ridge of its high back across her shoulder blades. Soon, she was sure, it was going to be almost impossible to believe what she had just heard from Marcus.

CHAPTER SIX

IT was a long and totally unreal day for Sally. There was lunch outdoors with an effervescent Viola and a smiling, watchful Josef; Katarina serving them herself, while the *señora* slept, because she liked Josef to have the titbits he preferred. There was a strange, hazy afternoon in the garden and then tea alone with her mother.

Viola, dabbing her neatly crimsoned mouth with a wisp of lace, said this was certainly the life, wasn't it, darling? "You go on for year after monotonous year, comparatively happy—because you've no experience of anything different. I'm not being disloyal to your father, Sally, but he was rather stuck in a groove, and because I was so fond of him he kept me there with him. Once he'd given me the continental honeymoon I wanted, Devonshire and the Lakes were as far as he wanted to go, and frankly, I used to find our annual leave rather a bore. I longed for something that I knew must exist, and now I've found it, right here on San Palos!"

"You wouldn't be so keen on the island if the Navy weren't here."

"No, of course not. They turn Naval Town into a busy little slice of England, and the officers are great fun. If you hadn't been snatched by Marcus I could have found you a nice husband among them. Mind you, they get a bit serious at times. At the moment they're worked up because one of their launches was stolen the other day. It turned up again, but it had been used by someone who had no respect for Navy property. Seems that so far they haven't had to guard their small craft, but they're setting a watch, now." She sighed, but not deeply. "You can't imagine anything really horrid happening on San Palos, can you? Lilac harvest, grape harvest, wine-making, *fiestas* . . . work and play, but no intrigue."

Only private intrigue, thought Sally despondently. She looked up at the Mauresque artistry of the balcony arches, saw Josef gazing enigmatically down at them, and shifted her glance to the trailing plants about the lily-pool at the other side of the courtyard. The sun was shining over there, causing blinding little flashes of lights where it slanted over the faint ripples.

This wasn't the first time she had felt out of tune with her mother, but she had never before felt so blankly and desperately alone. "Are you staying in this evening?" she asked.

"No, I'm going to some sort of social affair in the town. We were all invited, as a matter of fact—you and Marcus as well, but as Marcus is tied up . . ." She broke off and resumed happily, "Why not come, anyway? There's quite a number of spare men."

Why not, indeed? What could she do here, but palpitate all alone in her room? "Yes, I'd like to come," she said quickly. "You wear blue and I'll wear the pink and brown. We may shake them a little!"

But somehow the evening didn't come alive for Sally. She saw fresh-faced naval men, some wives and a few island girls with their *duennas,* was danced with and chattered to, given drinks, cigarettes and several compliments. Coming home there was a bright waning moon over the trees and the sound of a breeze through the valleys, the scent of lilac, the caressing feel of the Mediterranean spring. But a shutter had come down between Sally and the outside world. When she reached her bedroom she was isolated, wide awake, with her thoughts.

Her brain was working now with frightening clarity. Marcus had asked her to marry him. He wasn't in love with her—didn't even pretend to be—and he had no notion that she was in love with him, but he was willing, coolly and efficiently, to make her his wife and the mistress of Las Viñas.

Examined dispassionately, it wasn't so amazing as it had at first appeared. True, she was only nineteen, knew very little Spanish and nothing about running such a household. But circumstances had thrust her, metaphorically as well as literally, into his arms. So that an old, frail woman should not be shocked into an attack which might kill her, Sally had consented to a few weeks' engagement. She hadn't liked the idea, but there had been no harm intended by the deception, only good. At the end of a month or so she would have regretfully decided that she could not make Marcus happy, have withdrawn from the household and made private plans for the future.

But in view of the doctor's verdict, that couldn't happen now. Doña Inez's health was more finely balanced upon her emotions than even Marcus had thought. It would be quite easy to argue that Doña Inez was no concern of Sally's, that she couldn't have her future dictated by solicitude for an elderly Spanish woman she had known for only a couple of weeks. Yes, quite easy — but nothing could alter the fact that Sally had come to like the old *señora* and feel more than liking for Marcus. They were complications she could not ignore; they colored everything.

For Marcus, she thought bitterly, everything had become clear-cut. After his talk with Carlos he had considered the whole situation with clinical thoroughness; he would have made an excellent surgeon. Back in England, two or three months ago, he had cut adrift from the woman he had meant to marry. In his way he had loved her—no doubt about that. A man like Marcus wouldn't travel to England for one particular woman unless she meant more to him than any other woman in the world. It had probably irked him that she was an actress; he had even told Sally, off-handedly, that Nadine was not a good actress; yet the press cutting Sally had found had praised Nadine, though briefly. Marcus had disliked Nadine's profession and perhaps naturally had thought she would give it up for him. Her refusal to do so would have jarred something deep within him, his overpowering masculinity and the touch of Spanish blood that made it imperative for his wife to be all woman and his possession.

So he had put Nadine behind him. It couldn't have been easy and the effort had left him cool and uncaring. Some time, he had decided, he would marry a Spanish girl; that was that.

Then, quite suddenly, the incident of the tipsy Jim McCartney and the news that Doña Inez had been stricken. And there he was, at Las Viñas with a pseudo-fiancée and her mother, being kind and considerate, grave about Doña Inez and gently mocking at the dining table when guests congratulated him and told him that Sally was a lovely surprise. Had Sally been in the mood for it, she could have had heaps of private enjoyment with Marcus over the situation.

But the worst had happened. Marcus had not remained the aloof man who had made her uneasy; he had become closer and more comprehensible. His proprietorial pose had awakened her, his lightest touch held magnetism, and the mere suggestion of intimacy brought her heart into her throat. Shatteringly, she had fallen in love with a man who had no use for a loving woman.

And now, because he had to marry some time and Sally had the *señora's* welfare in her hands, he had decided that marriage with her might suit him very well. A six months' engagement, he had said. Just long enough for her to become well known on the island and decisively introduced to his various sets of relations, near and distant. Just long enough for the atmosphere of Las Viñas to seep into her, for the idea of becoming a del Moscado Durant to grow into the most desirable goal on earth. He'd be a devoted husband; no doubt about that.

Pacing her bedroom, Sally tried to see herself as Marcus's wife. It was impossible. As a genuine fiancée, then. That was less difficult, but she could visualize it only as a rather bleak relationship because in an engagement two hearts explore each other with love and tenderness and understanding; one heart struggling alone would be a forlorn thing. And yet . . .

Perhaps because she wanted it so much, Sally compelled her thoughts into more hopeful channels. Love begets love, so they say. If she showed him, gradually, that her heart was brimming and her life full, because of him, surely Marcus would come to respond? With care and as much understanding as she could muster she might be able to make herself indispensable to him, and while she waited for his love there would be the warmth of friendship, the belonging, the slender bond between them which must surely strengthen with time?

Sally undressed and put out the light, went into her balcony and looked over a world of black trees, of indigo sky lit by a moon she could not see. She leant on the wall and looked down at the eerie darkness of the garden and the wedge of courtyard that was visible from this angle. And almost without volition, her gaze shifted towards other balconies. There was no light in Marcus's room, no light anywhere. It was two o'clock, and she ought to have been in bed like the others. Was Marcus awake? Was he lying in one of those great ornate beds with his hands under his head and a gaze fixed upon the ceiling? Or, having made his own decision, was he calmly awaiting hers, and sleeping peacefully at this moment?

In a wave of ungoverned imagination she saw him slicking back his dark hair in front of a bedroom mirror, saw him turning and leaning over her with that tolerant, knowledgeable smile on his lips. He'd make love as he did everything else, expertly. She shivered, and oddly she remembered a lecturer at St. Alun's telling the student nurses: "Don't give your heart to nursing—give your body and your brain. It's not difficult to become expert at something that doesn't touch the heart. In the nursing profession we want experts." That was the lecturer's opinion, of course, and Sally hadn't entirely agreed with it.

A little blindly, she shook her head. She was getting mixed up now, sliding away from the subject because she was tired. And yet she was sure she wouldn't sleep, because there was still the other side of things to mull over. Supposing she stood out for the keeping of their first bargain. A week from now she would be free of Las Viñas, free to work at the nursing home, though it was far more likely that she would go home and complete her training. And ahead there wouldn't only be the loneliness and wretchedness Marcus had mentioned; there'd be the haunting knowledge that she needn't have been lonely and full of grief.

She could have had a gracious home near her mother, and a small part of Marcus. *Anything* here at Las Viñas was better than nothing at all in England.

From the corner of her eye she caught a movement below, and turned her head. Someone had appeared there, a man wearing a dark jacket over a white shirt and slacks. She peered down and saw it was Josef, and in almost the same moment he raised his head and saw her. For a second he hesitated, and then he came to the flagstones just under her balcony and spoke up to her, softly.

"You, too, are unable to sleep, *señorita*? You are feeling as despondent as I?" She shook her head and gestured him to silence, but had no time to move back before he added, "I have not yet forgiven myself for speaking as I did this morning. Much as I desire to remain here and get to work, I will leave San Palos if it embarrasses you. I mean it, with all my heart."

She shook her head again, whispered, "Goodnight," and went into her room, pulling the french window closed behind her.

The small encounter jolted her memory. She heard Josef's hot pronouncement in his own room: "Marcus wants only a mistress for his house, a mother for his children. His whole life is the estate of Las Viñas and that actress in London!"

That actress in London. Marcus had business interests in England, was bound to go over there occasionally. Nadine Carmody knew all about those interests, and if she cared for Marcus she would see him again. She might even be the sort of woman who'd prefer him to be married. A career for herself, a lover . . .

Sally crawled exhaustedly into bed. You can't have it all ways, my girl, she told herself hollowly. If you want the man you have to take his background as well. But you don't have to take another woman, not if you're canny and feminine and determined.

Sally had never felt less determined in her life. When sleep eventually stole over her she only knew that she loved

Marcus wholly and desperately. Her problem was no nearer solution than that; or so she thought.

*   *   *

During the next few days the whole atmosphere at Las Viñas became subtly lightened. Josef borrowed a car and went out a good deal, Viola was expansively ecstatic about the opening of her flower counter next Monday, Doña Inez merged her birdlike watchfulness with benign content, and even Katarina was seen to smile dourly and help the other servants when she was free. But it was Marcus's attitude that helped Sally most.

After that painful interview she had not seen him till next day at lunch. It was windy, and they had all lunched together in the dining room: Marcus and Sally, Carlos, Josef, Viola, Captain Northwick and a shipping agent named Essler who obviously thought Viola Sheppard the wittiest and most attractive woman on earth.

Sally was wearing a print frock, splashes of orange and black on white, and maybe the brilliance of color contrast had detracted from the small amount of pink in her cheeks. Through lack of sleep there were dark smudges under her eyes, but knowing that cowardice wouldn't help she met Marcus's glance squarely. He smiled reassuringly, spoke to her in warm tones that all could hear.

"Did you get my message? As it was so windy I thought we'd drop the idea of going to the beach this morning and have a picnic tea this afternoon instead. There are several spots where you can get right away from the breeze. Any of you others care to come?"

All were in favor except Carlos. "I have been here at Las Viñas so much lately that my records are suffering. I must certainly attack them strongly this afternoon."

So they had eaten and chatted, rested, tidied up and spread themselves out in two cars. And during the whole of that afternoon, while they drove through vineyards and cruised along coastal roads that gave magnificent vistas, while they drank tea and ate sandwiches and sweet cakes, and strolled among the rock plants and carob and wild figs, Marcus was charming and mocking and very much the thoughtful host and overlord. There was no marring incident. Even when Josef Carvallo mentioned at one spot that they were close to the clay-field, and that he knew of a small place which he could rent, Marcus commented upon it without sarcasm.

"We could probably make a go of a small pottery industry," he said. "But it wouldn't be any use producing till you were sure of a market throughout the Mediterranean. Why not give Essler some copies of your designs? He could sound the market for you."

Josef looked slightly stunned. "Do I have to thank Sally for this? Has she been interceding for me?"

Marcus smiled. "She's on your side, of course; you look appealing since you cracked your head. But she hasn't been begging for you."

"Then perhaps the good Doña Inez!" He sighed. "She hardly spoke when I saw her this morning."

"She hasn't weighed you up yet. I've never been against your going in for ceramics—only against your starting something you might get tired of."

"I shall not tire of it," said Josef quickly. "The small house I wish to rent is one of yours, Marcus. The old people are moving out to live with a daughter and the place will be empty. I could use the lower rooms as the factory and live above them."

"No harm in that. You can even put in some equipment and start preparing your clay, if you like. Use it as a hobby to keep you going till we hear Essler's findings. If you made a few articles, experimentally, Northwick could probably take them for his store. They'll sell to tourists."

"And when I need money for a mill and tools and wages?" Josef asked cautiously.

"It'll be available—to you or to anyone else who's willing to develop an industry that will benefit the island."

Josef did not press his luck beyond that point. Looking over her shoulder at him, Sally saw that his smooth Latin face hadn't yet lost the expression of blank incredulity—or was it puzzlement? She glanced at Marcus, saw a smile on his lips and caught a half wink when he briefly turned his head her way. The weighty feeling round her heart eased a little.

There were other guests that evening, among them Pedro and Isabel Suarez. The woman's guttural, crooning speech was a tenuous link between Marcus and Sally. We're actually sharing small jokes, Sally thought tremulously; can it last?

There were several guests next day, and the day after. It seemed accidental that she and Marcus were never alone together, but she knew he was arranging things that way. He jollied her into playing cards, into bathing from the pale, rock-strewn beach. With others, they watched the lilac-picking.

"See how cleverly it's done?" he said, as he stood beside her at the edge of the forest of pale mauve blossom. "A snip, and the spray drops straight into the basket that hangs from the shoulder. Most of them use small pruning scissors for the job, but some of the older hands refuse them. They swear there's nothing like their horny old thumbnails for speed and accuracy."

Except for two or three boys, the pickers were women of all ages. They were dressed in their oldest cottons and the flat, home-made sandals of the island. The sun was warm, but not sufficiently strong to force the wearing of headgear. Glossy black curls and iron-grey knots moved among the laden branches, but a burst of song was often the only indication that a picker was near.

"The scent is almost stupefying, isn't it?" she said. "And the sprays are so lush. I wish English people could see it. Have you ever sent any over by air?"

She meant commercially, but the moment she had spoken she realized he could infer something else. There seemed to be an imperceptible pause before he answered pleasantly,

"Yes, I've sent a box or two to friends. I send grapes too. If they go out by ferry on the day they're picked and catch the plane at Majorca they reach the addressee within twenty-four hours—still warm from the San Palos sun!"

Well, there was bound to be a bit of thin ice about. Trust Marcus to skim round it with the minimum of delay. She turned to her mother.

"Would you like to post some lilac to one or two people in England?"

"I don't think so, darling. It's awfully naughty of me, but I've decided I won't bother to keep in touch. Have you written many letters?"

"Only a few, to friends at St. Alun's."

"Do you want to send them some lilac?" asked Marcus.

"Not all of them. There's one who has a birthday about now, and I'm sure she'd like it. The others would wonder if Shep had lost her mind—sending flowers to nurses who have more than enough to do with them on duty—but Betty's different. She and I used to . . ."

"Yes?" prompted Marcus, as she halted.

Viola waved airily. "They were wild flower enthusiasts — the first celandine, the first violet, the first primrose. I remember Sally crouching over a snowdrop that had pushed its way through slush in our tiny garden. She needed some new woollies at the time, but the sight of that rash little snowdrop meant more than if she'd been given a cheque for twenty pounds!"

"Good for Sally," said Marcus quietly, looking at her pink cheeks and lowered eyelids. "Write a note and give it to me. I'll have some lilac picked first thing on Monday morning and kept on ice till it's delivered to the ferry at eleven."

"You spoil her," said Viola. "But you spoil me too, so I've no grouse. Except that I've really had enough of staring at this sea of lilac, and the donkeys they use for transport do come uncomfortably close. May we go now?"

They were given cups of chocolate and almond fancies by Señora Suarez and eventually got back into the cars. The others were going straight back to town, so only Viola and Sally accompanied Marcus, and Viola, as usual, was in the front seat.

"Have you seen my little bower at the store, Marcus?" she asked as they wound down the lovely scented road.

When he had nodded she went on, "From Monday, I shall be going down every morning for three hours. I shall only work in the afternoons when I have an order to decorate a house or a hall for some event. I've been wondering what I shall do for transport. Captain Northwick would arrange it for me, but I don't want to depend on him outside the business."

Marcus slanted her a mocking glance. "That's very wise. If you grant too many favors to the Captain, the other one, Essler, will conclude that you've made your choice. And you haven't yet, have you?"

Viola gave her high-pitched, bell-like laugh. "Don't tease about such things, Marcus. They're both very nice, but I hardly know them. I owe nothing to Mr. Essler, and if I can show only a small profit to the Captain I shan't be at all in his debt. In any case, as I pointed out to him at the beginning, the people who come in to buy flowers might easily stroll through the rest of the store and buy something else that they hadn't really intended to buy. So he won't know just how profitable the flower department will be."

"That's surprisingly shrewd of you. I've an idea that you can already do as you like with the Captain."

"Which is another reason why I'd rather not ask more favors of him."

"Well, we can arrange transport. One of the gardeners is a good driver, and he'll take you down and pick you up every day."

"That's sweet of you, dear, but it won't quite do. You see, I already have a few nice orders, and right from the start I'll need a car. I do drive, you know. Of course, I could make use of the Casa Northwick utility, but it would be restricting because I could only have it when it's free. I was wondering whether I could use the small car that Josef Carvallo drives sometimes. He could have it most afternoons."

Sally leaned forward anxiously. "Mother, don't you think the business should pay for your transport?"

"Frankly," said Viola, smiling blandly, "I don't think it will be able to stand the expense for some time. Marcus understands—don't you, Marcus?"

"Perfectly," he said. "Use the small car, by all means. Josef is moving out, anyway."

"To that house you said he could have?" asked Sally curiously.

He nodded and turned his head slightly, so that she could hear him. "I told him that if he can get established in a small way without any further help from me, I'll see that he gets all the financial help he needs for expansion. All I want is proof that the leopard has changed his spots."

"You don't believe he has, do you?"

"No, but it's one case in which I'll be glad to be proved wrong. It'll be good to have him out of the house, anyway."

"Sally will miss him," said Viola. "She and Josef always seem able to find something to talk about. And they have secrets too. Don't you, darling?"

"What secrets?" asked Marcus non-committally.

"None that I can remember," said Sally.

"Oh, dear, have I made a blue?" queried Viola contritely. "Let's forget it, then."

"What secrets?" repeated Marcus.

Viola flung a penitent look at Sally before she answered him. "It was only something Katarina told me. She said that the other night Doña Inez needed one of her pills and there were none left in the bedroom, so she went to get a new supply from somewhere or other. It was in the early hours and everyone should have been sleeping, but she heard voices, and traced them to Sally's balcony. Being nosey, or worried, or something, she went further, and saw Sally in her balcony talking down to Josef in the *patio*."

There was a brief silence during which Sally sat, a little numb, waiting for whatever might come next.

"Why did Katarina tell you that?" asked Marcus, still without expression.

Viola shrugged distastefully. "It's nothing, Marcus. I do hate servants' gossip and I had no intention of mentioning it to anyone at all — not even to Sally. I'm sure I don't want our relationships upset in any way."

"You haven't said why Katarina told you," Marcus persisted, in those even tones. "She's Spanish, and I can understand that the incident might have disturbed her, but did she explain why she came to you—not to anyone else?"

"Because I'm Sally's mother, I suppose," said Viola, quite upset at her own stupidity. "She said she had no wish to spy, that what Sally and Josef had said to each other was harmless, but that she thought I ought to know, so that I could watch, and warn Sally against indiscretion."

"And you didn't warn Sally," he said inexorably.

"Of course not. Sally and Josef may play together, but that's all. I was sure there must be some very simple explanation, and to be quite honest I forgot it — till it slipped out just now."

Marcus didn't say anything more, and from the angle at which he held his head it was impossible to see whether he had completely lost the new urbanity. The car purred down the hillside into grape country, took the long winding lane to Las Viñas. It was Friday, the day when the fishermen loaded their catch into baskets, slung them across their donkeys' backs and trudged all over the island, selling in the villages; they waved as the car passed them. There would be langouste cooked in wine for lunch today; the thought of it made Sally feel rather sick.

It was a relief, when they arrived at Las Viñas, to find a couple of naval men waiting for Marcus in the courtyard. They bowed to the two women, spoke to him at once.

"We caught a chap in one of our launches—didn't seem to be doing anything queer, but he was a civilian on official property, which is an offence. We took him up to the office for questioning to see if he knew anything about the launch that was borrowed without permission a week ago, but he's asked for his rights—to be questioned in the presence of the San Palos magistrate. If you can come down now, Mr. Durant, it could probably be cleared up in ten minutes."

Marcus nodded. "I'll come in my own car." To Sally and Viola he said, "I'll be back for lunch. So long."

Sally watched the two cars slide away and then she turned to where Viola sat under the palms. Her mother looked at her brightly.

"Sorry about that gaffe, darling. I was thinking so busily about the car Marcus promised me, and flower decorations for the Naval Ball, that I didn't really know what I was saying, till it was out. But don't worry. Marcus knows you too well to care about a tiny lapse on your part." Adroitly, she changed the subject. "Did you know he's a magistrate? Doesn't it thrill you enormously to know you're going to marry such a man? If only I'd had such luck at your age!"

Smarting as much for her father's memory as for any hurt to herself, Sally nodded and went indoors to wash the smell of lilac from her fingers.

*   *   *

During that weekend there was a faint dampness in the air and a haze hid the sun. A servant told Sally it meant the end of spring and the beginning of summer. On San Palos, April was glorious with summer flowers, the first fruit and a huge variety of salads and vegetables. At the end of June it became really hot and July and August were the "full months," when fields and vines became bare through harvesting, the earth could be ploughed and the winter crops sown. Two complete seasons of growth, and except for heavier rains the winter was warm and springlike.

Josef Carvallo left Las Viñas unobtrusively. No goodbyes, of course, because he would look in for a meal now and then, and to report progress. With her mother, Marcus and Captain Northwick, Sally drove out to the mansion of a retired Catalan business man for dinner on Saturday, and on Sunday a dozen people came to Las Viñas for lunch.

Marcus was charming to everyone, protective and considerate towards Sally. That afternoon, while others rested, was the first time they had found themselves alone since he had proposed turning the sham engagement into a genuine one. They went down into the garden, walked among the flower beds towards the cypresses, without talking much. Sally guessed he was trying her out. For nearly a week they had been together for much of every day. For fifteen minutes each morning they had visited Doña Inez, and each time they left the *señora's* room his arm had lain across her shoulder as he pushed her gently in front of him into the corridor. There had been guests galore to see the proprietorial glances, and one gift from him, an impersonal tooled leather writing case packed out with writing materials and with a gold pen and pencil tucked into the appropriate slots.

Now he offered cigarettes and lighted hers before setting the flame to his own. Her hand must have trembled slightly, for he stated calmly.

"I'll definitely leave it to you to reopen the subject, so stop quivering. What I have to speak about now is only vaguely connected with the thing you haven't quite accepted. You always look very sweet, but I'd have to be blind and insensitive not to notice that you ring the changes on half a dozen frocks. I want you to get more clothes, Sally."

She looked down at the path as they moved. "Very well."

Her reply must have surprised him slightly, for a moment or two elapsed before he said, "A few days ago I asked Northwick to telegraph a Barcelona fashion house to send sketches of stuff they have on hand. He's received them, and if you'll choose what you'd like and give the series of measurements they ask for, they'll alter their models accordingly before sending them over with matching underwear and shoes. You're not to have any silly ideas about accepting the things."

"I shan't mind wearing your gifts here at your house," she said, low-voiced.

He took this in, but did not comment. "Then that's settled. Northwick left the sketches with me and I'll send them to your room. Make it at least six outfits, and choose some sort of ball gown thing in white, that you can wear at the Lilac Fiesta."

"I'll do that."

"Good." He paused. "There's just one thing I may not have made quite clear enough. When we're officially engaged I'll make no more demands on you than I'm making at the moment. That will come gradually, as you become ready for it."

And as *he* became ready for it, Sally thought bleakly. He had no more wish to make love to her than she had to be made love to by someone whose heart wasn't in it. Apparently he expected no reply to that, for when they had covered a few more yards he began explaining the history of the gardens. They were back on the slightly formal, very pleasant footing which had prevailed during the last few days.

Viola's first day at the store was a moderate success, her second very dull and her third not much better. Then on Thursday things began to look up for the weekend; the Naval Ball on Friday and a wedding anniversary party on Saturday. At Las Viñas she was preoccupied, but she did mention that Captain Northwick was expecting Sally for lunch on Saturday.

Marcus had a court session of sorts that Saturday morning and he had been invited to stay for luncheon with the business and naval men of the town. So Viola and Sally drove alone to the square cottage that bulged with nautical monstrosities. But Sally noticed that quite a few of the prints had disappeared from the walls, and the pot of basil had been superseded by a few stiff sprays of pink oleander.

Viola was kind enough not to mention any specific alteration. "You seem much cosier here, Captain," she said in her smiling, chatty way. "But you won't mind if I sit with my back to the brass lamp, will you? What is it made of— a piece of deck-rail?"

The Captain, to his credit, took this stoically. Sally was sure the lamp would be cast into the limbo which now held the discarded prints before Viola came again to the cottage. It was really amazing what her mother could accomplish with a single comment. Before the Captain even got round to wondering whether he'd have the courage to think seriously about Mrs. Sheppard, she would have groomed his abode into a presentable, perhaps even acceptable, background for a wife. And he wouldn't even know it had been happening.

Maybe it was typical of the queer, hazy mood which was so difficult to throw off, that Sally should come round to regarding the idea of her mother's marrying again without distaste. In England, Viola had been fretful and unwell, longing so much to get away that she had paid fifty pounds she couldn't easily afford for a nebulous job in Barcelona and uprooted Sally from St. Alun's. Magically, her mood had lightened during the cruise, and now, secure in a luxury post and playing off a middle-aged business man against a retired naval captain, she was in her element as she had never been before.

Viola had loved her husband as much as it was in her nature to love anyone, but Sally realized now, when her mother was expanding so happily in the sunshine and masculine admiration, that the quiet suburban life of the Sheppards must have irked Viola unbearably as a newly-wed after a continental honeymoon she must have been wildly happy; no doubt she had imagined life would be a long succession of honeymoons in exciting places, with Richard taking charge, smoothing the edges everywhere, providing a warm and dependable cocoon. Sally had long ago concluded that her father had worked harder than was normal, so that Viola should go short of nothing she had been used to before her marriage. She thought, a little achingly, of the disillusionment he must have known when, because it was all he could afford, he had taken Viola to Wastwater or Clovelly, and been rewarded by bored sighs.

There was one thing Sally had become sure of on San Palos. Her mother fitted into the island as she had never fitted into the London set; she was like a jewel set in platinum.

After lunch, the Captain took them for a drive out to one of the bays. For exercise, Sally went off along the beach and climbed the rocks which gave a view of the lighthouse she sometimes saw from her window as a wheeling light.

When she got back to the car the others were missing, so she sat inside and waited, watching the curling waves and the lift of the sand in the wind. A couple of island girls in full skirts and blouses went down to paddle and look for shellfish, and not far away some boys eyed them and laughed loudly together to draw the girls' attention. But when the two walked demurely back up the beach the lads were looking the other way. That was convention on San Palos.

It was nearly five when Viola and the Captain returned from their jaunt. Sally suspected it had not been too successful, for Viola hated walking and the Captain was averse to sitting on rocks.

Viola said, "The Captain is going to take me down to the hall, so that I can give the final touch to the decorations. Going with us, Sally?"

"No, I'd better get back. You're invited as guests to that anniversary party, aren't you?"

"Yes. The Captain says he'll wait for me at the hall and take me home to dress. He's going to call for me later, too."

"And what are you doing this evening, Miss Sally?" asked the Captain, in his courteous, stilted tones. "I believe Marcus has an uncle arriving from Majorca?"

"The uncle is bringing other guests—they're only staying a few days, though. They're due to arrive this afternoon."

"I'll take you home at once, then." He smiled paternally. "They've probably come to see *you.*"

She smiled at him and shook her head. "They've been waiting for Doña Inez to be well enough to see them. She's done splendidly during the past two weeks and Dr. Suarez said it would be good for her to have more visitors; she wants them, herself."

Viola said urgently, "You must slip indoors the back way and dress up a bit before you meet them, Sally. Drive on, Captain."

At Las Viñas they left Sally at the foot of the steps. It wasn't necessary for her to use the back entrance, for the courtyard was empty, and when she paused in the hall there came no sound from the *sala.* If the guests had arrived they were upstairs in their rooms. She went up quietly and closed herself within her bedroom. She had a bath and put on a slim-fitting black lace frock. Black didn't suit her so well as it suited some blondes, but when she had to meet elderly Spaniards it was safe. She brushed the blown sand from her hair, pressed the waves softly about her brow and temples, used lipstick and a touch of mascara. It was only six and golden sunlight still slanted across the trees, but perhaps she ought to go down.

Ought? She felt cold as she stood still and contemplated the word. She seemed to have lost all inclination to assert herself. And she knew why. Whatever happened on San Palos, however she was bruised and beaten, she couldn't give up yet, if ever. Life with Marcus promised to be arid and painful. Without him it would be plain hell.

There was a knock at the door. *"Señorita!"*

Sally turned the handle and smiled automatically at the bobbing maid. "Yes, Carmelita?"

"I am to ask you to go down to the *sala*, please. *Ahora, señorita.*"

Sally thanked her, came from the room and walked down the staircase. There were sounds now in the *sala*—several voices discreetly subdued. The door was ajar, and as she pushed it wide Marcus was there, slipping a hand under her arm and squeezing a warning. Sally saw two men bowing towards her, two seated women inclining their heads and smiling. Then, almost precipitately, she stopped.

There was another chair, tall-backed and with a matching stool close to it. And seated there, wrapped in regal black with a band of diamonds at her scrawny little neck and Carlos hovering close by, was Doña Inez!

CHAPTER SEVEN

MARCUS was saying, so that no one but Sally could hear it, "It surprised me too, but take it in your stride. She's done this solely for us, so we must make it worth her while."

The old *señora's* small cackling laugh broke in. "Come and greet me, my child, before Marcus introduces you to my cousin. He is my young cousin, hardly more than seventy, and he has lived on Majorca since he married forty years ago." She looked appraisingly at Sally. "Yes, you will suit this room. It badly needs the young face."

"Do you feel quite well down here, Doña Inez?" asked Sally anxiously. "Not even a little bit dizzy?"

The *señora* made a feeble snapping noise with her fingers. "You and Carlos! If I knew so much about the human body I might scare myself into dizziness. I feel good!"

The introductions followed. Don Antonio . . . Doña Esmeralda . . . Doña Bianca . . . Don Nicolas. All of them charming and old, wearing black clothes that looked new. Marcus, too, was wearing a black dinner jacket, and though he looked more hawk-nosed and arresting than ever, Sally couldn't help feeling an hysterical desire to laugh. This was supposed to be a jolly occasion, and everyone had chosen black; the oddest angle of it was that no one but herself noticed it.

Marcus poured wine, very little for his grandmother but the usual generous amount for the guests. He put Sally's glass into her hand, bent a most handsome smiling profile towards Doña Inez and said.

"We will drink to you, *madrecita.* There is nothing I have wanted more than to see you in your own chair, among us. To your health."

Doña Inez accepted this with a smile on her little aged bird's face. When everyone had echoed Marcus's sentiment and sipped, she nodded with satisfaction. "And now we old ones will drink to the young," she said. "To Marcus and his betrothed—their future." When the toast had been drunk she let Marcus take her glass and her little claws hooked themselves together as they always did when she had a pronouncement to make. "This Carlos has allowed me one hour in this room, and already half of that time has gone. So we must approach our happy business, and I will leave you to celebrate with other guests who will be arriving later." She paused, took a breath and, looking at Marcus, added quietly, "I must thank you from the heart for your patience during the past weeks. For me, you have postponed the enjoyment of your fiancée. And you, my dear Sally, have been gentle and willing to wait till the old woman is well enough for the great occasion."

"You're talking a great deal too much," Marcus said mildly. "Don Antonio will be here for three days. Why get everything said at once?"

"Because," the dark eyes flashed their unquenchable fire, "I will have you miss nothing of the decorum that should attend your betrothal. Where is Mrs. Sheppard?"

"She's out," said Sally quickly. "If she'd known . . ."

"It does not matter. I suspect that your mother has small use for the customs of the del Moscados. However, to us they mean much, and in time they will mean a great deal to you also. Come and stand close to me. You too, Marcus."

He took his time, asked carelessly, "Why the melodrama? You've done enough for one evening."

"*Valgame Dios!*" she said fiercely, and glared round at her relatives. "You did well to have no Englishmen in your families. They have iron instead of marrow in their bones."

Carlos bent and patted her shoulder. "Marcus is right, *tia mia*. You are talking too much on this first occasion downstairs. Tomorrow . . ."

"Tomorrow I shall be too tired to come down. Very well, let us get to business." Her hands were grasping a small black sequinned bag which had been indistinguishable on her lap. She opened it, spoke thinly but clearly to the people grouped round her. "Some days ago Marcus and I discussed the betrothal rings and I persuaded him to make his choice of the family jewels. He selected the square emerald which was my mother's and a signet ring which belonged to his English grandfather." The voice quavered. "This is my happiest moment. Take the rings, Marcus."

He must have realized moments ago what was happening. Sally herself had half guessed it, but even so the shock was like a bludgeon. She felt numb and trapped. Her lips must have been parted, tensely, for a long minute; they now felt cold and dry and lifeless.

Then Doña Inez spoke again. "My dear, you will change the little ring I gave you to the other hand. Now, Marcus."

Afterwards Sally wondered if she could have acted in some way to prevent the scene going any further, and she decided that she had had no alternative but to accept the signet ring and give Marcus her left hand. She never remembered slipping the heavy gold ring on to Marcus's finger, and even that second in which he had gently pushed the emerald down over her knuckle seemed to pass without her being aware of it. She heard him say something in Spanish to Doña Inez, felt his light salute on each cheek which the others no doubt expected, and automatically bent for the old *señora's* kiss.

"So," said Doña Inez shakily. "It is done, and I shall rest the better for knowing it." She looked up at them both as they stood close to her, "You two must be happy—not worry over the old grandmother who has already lived too long. I am happier than I have been for very many years. Now, you will go outside, while I suffer the indignity of being carried to my bed."

Marcus smiled at her with a tenderness that Sally found painful. "I don't know how you got down here, but I'm going to take you up myself. Come, *madrecita*."

The tiny figure was so light that he gathered her up easily. She was smiling tiredly but with infinite pride as she nodded goodnight and closed her eyes. Marcus bore her from the room, with Carlos close behind him.

In the *sala* there was an awkward spell of silence. Then, courteously, one of the women begged Sally to seat herself and tell them how she felt about living in San Palos. But before she had spoken more than a dozen words the first of the dinner guests arrived and she was in the unusual position of having to make the introductions. Nearly twenty minutes passed before she could slip outside into the cloistered terrace that edged the courtyard for a breathing space.

It was almost dark and a star or two already winked above the trees. Sally clasped her fingers and felt the two rings: the delicate sapphire and the heavy, diamond-circled emerald. Neither ring was hers by right; only the woman Marcus loved should wear them — with a brimming gladness and pride.

She moved along in the dimness, through an archway into the small *patio* below the *señora's* bedroom. There she stopped and looked up. There was a small soft light in the room at the top of the steps and for some time she stared at that illumined french window without moving. Someone appeared on the balcony: Katarina.

The woman saw her and came down. The yellow face looked a little ghastly in the heavy dusk, but there was a smile on the brown lips and her tones sounded deliberate and sincere.

"I was in the *señora's* confidence, *señorita,* and helped to take her down to the *sala.* May I offer my felicitations?"

"Thank you, Katarina. Is she all right—Doña Inez?"

"Tired, that is all. But she was determined, and Dr. Suarez felt it would do more harm to deny her what she wanted so much. I am sure you and Don Marcus are going to be most happy here. I hope it for you; believe that."

Why did she harp on it? Sally wondered dispiritedly, but not for long. Perhaps she heard doubts in other people's voices because stronger doubts were so deeply embedded within herself.

"You're very kind, Katarina."

"May I suggest something—that you take off the small ring given by the *señora?* For tonight, only the engagement ring, no?"

"I was going to do that. I'm going up to my room the back way." And she nodded and left the *señora's* companion.

In her room, Sally was tempted to change the black lace frock for something brighter, but she felt too peculiar inside herself to make the decision. She tidied her hair, used a compact, slipped the small ring into a drawer and switched off the light. But before going below she stepped out on to the balcony. It was quite dark now and a breeze was moving the tops of the palms and magnolias. Below the courtyard a garden light illumined the tops of the guests' cars and down the drive another post shed light across the drive. Someone was walking quickly down the drive towards the gate. Josef? It looked like him, but she knew he hadn't been invited this evening. Perhaps he had been up to beg something from Marcus.

Again the tips of her fingers sought the unfamiliar ring, and she became aware of a raw ache in her throat. She hadn't had to decide after all; it had been decided for her. She was engaged to Marcus, might even marry him. Not because of Doña Inez but because all this anguish, and all the pain of the future, would be easier to endure than cutting adrift and dying, emotionally.

She crossed the bedroom and went out into the ample light of the corridor. Viola was emerging from her own room, lovely in pastel pink brocade with a broad black collar, and carrying a slinky fur stole over her arm. She stopped as Sally reached her, looked at her unsmilingly and said,

"I've heard all about it. I'm glad for you, darling, but I do think it was rather dictatorial of the old woman. After all, it's the girl's parents who do the honors, not the man's grandmother. Show me the ring." She examined it and looked rather startled. "It must be worth thousands! Does it feel strange — wearing something so valuable?" She didn't wait for a reply. "Doña Inez might have made sure that I'd be in."

"I think it depended on Carlos's being here. It was a complete surprise to me."

"And to Marcus?"

"Yes. Please don't make any remarks about it."

"I shan't. But how do you think I feel—going out to someone else's anniversary party when I ought to be here at your celebration?"

"You and the Captain could dine here—send an apology."

"We'll do nothing of the sort. I'll give my own party for you and Marcus later on—and if I can avoid it, it won't be here at Las Viñas!"

"There's really nothing to be upset about. The *Señora* did what she felt she had to do because she felt capable of it this evening."

"She's an autocratic old eagle," said Viola crossly. "She knows I can't afford to give you the sort of wedding these del Moscados will expect, and she's decided that if they're footing the bill they'll also do things according to their own traditions. I'm sure Marcus will see that it's most unfair." It was only then that she bothered to take a good look at Sally's face. "You look dreadful—wearing black, too! If you'd only waited a day or two those outfits would have arrived from Barcelona. She's a selfish old tyrant, and if . . ."

"She's old and worn out," said Sally unsteadily, "and there's nothing you can do now it's over."

"No, I suppose not." Viola shrugged and the light habitual smile came back to her lips. "If you're satisfied, darling, why should I be distressed? I'm sure you'd much rather have had Marcus to yourself while you were exchanging rings—what a barbarous custom, by the way!— but perhaps you were fortunate in having so few to witness the event. Nothing's altered, really, is it? It's just that you have a much more expensive ring and Marcus is wearing something to show he's hooked." She looked at her diamond-framed watch. "I must go. Coming down?"

Together they descended the staircase, and in the hall they were met by Captain Northwick, who looked most distinguished in a light dinner jacket. He bowed, and then Marcus was there.

"Hallo," he said. "Can't we persuade you to stay in for dinner and go along to your party afterwards?"

Decisively, Viola shook her head. The pale lavender rinse had given way to pastel blue, and in the pink frock she looked pretty and doll-like, not a day over thirty-five. She raised a small white finger at Marcus.

"I'm a wee bit vexed over what's happening this evening. Personally, I've taken it that you two were officially engaged all the time—otherwise I couldn't have accepted your hospitality for so long, could I? But I do feel that when you were ready to call it official in your family you should have consulted me, so that I could have arranged a celebration elsewhere this evening. Your grandmother didn't consider me at all."

Marcus said easily, "It crept up on us, I'm afraid. Doña Inez suddenly felt up to tackling the thing, and she took Katarina and Carlos into her confidence—but no one else. She's too old to be judged, Viola."

"She did ask for you," said Sally in low tones to her mother. "You were out."

Slightly mollified, Viola patted her arm. Then she looked up at Marcus. "I'd better give you a motherly kiss, hadn't I? You know, I've just discovered that I couldn't possibly live here after your marriage. A huge son-in-law and grandchildren would wither me up in no time!"

She planted her small kiss and as an afterthought kissed Sally also. Then, with the Captain, she made her exit.

Marcus said quietly, "Feel all right?"

"Perfectly," answered Sally evenly.

"You looked terribly frightened in there, earlier. You mustn't be frightened."

"It was the shock."

"I didn't want anything like that to happen. I wanted you to tell me yourself—not to be forced into it."

"Yes, I know."

"On the whole, though, it may be as well things went the way they did."

"Perhaps."

"I knew you'd gone upstairs. I thought you might have changed your dress."

"Do you want me to?" she asked woodenly.

"Not now, it's too late. Come into the study for a minute."

She went with him into the room she seldom entered. The study was cosily lined with books and a couple of armchairs flanked the small ornate fireplace. From the drawer of the desk which stood close to the window Marcus took a flat black case. Sally looked at it and steeled herself. Marcus locked the drawer again and faced her.

"In our family we don't buy new engagement rings. It's thought that one of the family jewels has more meaning, more value. So instead I've bought you an engagement gift. It will probably look better with black than with any other color." He snapped open the case and showed her a collar of alternate pearls and diamonds. "Like it?"

"It's very beautiful," she said, without emotion.

"Then let's put it on, shall we?"

She turned obediently, but as his fingers touched her neck she shivered. Perhaps it was involuntarily that his fingers closed over her shoulder and gripped; certainly there was anger in the grip. With her head bent she waited for some swift exclamation from him, some eruption of the sudden violence she felt in his fingers. But he apparently took as firm a grasp on himself. His hand turned her and dropped to his side.

He appraised her coolly, her shoulders, the lovely thing about her slim white neck. "It's what the dress needs," he said. "They're waiting for us. We'd better join them."

A minute later Sally was entering the *sala* for the second time that evening, but this time she consciously kept her head high and did her utmost to look as sophisticated as the magnificent necklet and emerald ring she wore. But inside she was cold and scared.

On the whole the evening was not much different from other evenings at Las Viñas. The old uncle and his friends were travel-weary and excused themselves straight after dinner. The others chatted and drank, strolled outside and chatted and drank again. Towards midnight they straggled down the steps to their cars. Marcus accompanied them and Sally, after hesitating, went up to her room.

As she undressed there was a pain behind her eyes and a slackness in her limbs. She paused in the act of turning down the bed and ran her fingers through her short pale hair. How long would it be before she believed in the engagement? Did it really exist, that bond, or was it just another patch of unreality she had to live through? It had been a solemn moment down there, when Marcus had murmured something in Spanish and pressed the ring on to her finger, but try as she would she could not see herself married to him. The collaret—she looked at it as it lay on the dressing table—had been another piece of unreality. Such things weren't available on San Palos, so he must have bought it some time ago—perhaps in London, for Nadine Carmody. And there it had lain, nice and handy for presenting to the girl he had decided would do.

What in the world had happened to her spirit? she wondered. Being in love should have made her brave, not craven. But she had had too much to contend with; the weight of circumstances had smothered her and left her feeling as she felt now — not much more than half conscious and thoroughly enmeshed.

She stood staring at the wall beyond the bed, a cheerless churning in her head, her hands along the sides of her small pale face. She hardly heard the rap at the door and did not look round until whoever it was had entered. She gazed at Marcus blankly, from shadowed wood-violet eyes. In printed silk pyjamas, her hair tousled from her fingers and her face washed free of make-up, she looked small and appealing; even more so when she made an obvious effort to straighten up and appear normal.

He placed a glass of milk on the bedside table. "You ate very little at dinner, and I thought you'd better have this with a couple of aspirins." He paused. "You're not to worry about all this, Sally. Get into bed and go to sleep."

She spoke with some difficulty. "Marcus, I'm sorry I was a bit of an idiot this evening."

"You weren't an idiot. It was too much for you, and I was in the damnable position of being unable to do anything about it. But there's just one thing I've got to mention," he said, his voice tightening. "Don't shrink from me. For Doña Inez I can stand a good deal, but I'd better warn you that physical shrinking on your part might easily make me forget any promise I've made you. We're engaged, and when you're ready for it, we'll get married. I particularly wanted you to know tonight that you mean a lot to me."

She moistened her lips. "But nothing can alter the fact that the engagement was accidental, can it? If it had been some other girl with her mother on the 'Bellesta' . . ."

"No other girl and her mother would have been such babes adrift in Barcelona," said Marcus, with a faint smile.

"No, I suppose not. If you hadn't brought us to San Palos this situation would never have arisen. I did feel we owed you whatever I could do at the beginning, but . . . but it got beyond me."

"When I suggested we turn the engagement into a genuine one?"

She frowned down at the carpet. Her face looked suddenly thin and fine-drawn. "You see, I . . . I do believe in the love match, and I'm afraid I always will."

His tones became harsh. "There are a few things you're too young and innocent to have come up against yet. As I've said before, if you'd had an affair you'd view this whole thing differently. As you haven't, you feel you've missed something tremendous—some painfully sweet passion that would inevitably have drawn you into an idyllic marriage. You're capable of such love, Sally. I'm sure of that. What you're not aware of is that sometimes you have to choose your partner and let an engagement condition you for a good marriage. If you'll let yourself, you can be very happy almost at once."

She nodded again; her voice was husky. "I suppose what hurts is that feeling that I've missed something." She looked up, her eyes bright with pent-up tears. "Do you know what I wish? I wish I'd had time to fall headlong in love with Peter Malling. It wouldn't have mattered that he wasn't in love with me. I just wish there'd been a few more days, because I was falling pretty hard, and if I'd gone the whole way and then this had cropped up, I might not even have seen you as a man at all; I'd just have laughed my head off at anyone who'd mistaken me for your chosen girl from London, and then . . ."

"Stop it!"

But Sally was unwinding at last; she couldn't stop. "Anything I'd felt for Peter would have lasted just long enough, don't you see?" she choked. "I wouldn't have come to San Palos, because in Barcelona there would have been the chance of seeing him. I'd have got a job, any job, and I'd have watched the newspapers for details of his concerts. You couldn't have brought me here—I wouldn't have come! Don't you see that?" Furiously she brushed away the tears that had overflowed. "But because our poor little affair had to die off I was left at your mercy. You'd had a jolt to your self-esteem in England and were still smarting from it. When that horrible McCartney man . . ."

"Will you be quiet!" he blazed.

"No, I won't! You've had a lot of private revenge at my expense on that actress who let you down, and I've at least a right to say what I think. You don't have to promise me that you'll make yourself fall in love with me, and you don't have to school yourself into being quiet and controlled and understanding. And for the love of heaven don't ever give me that I'll-persuade-you-to-love-me line again. Nadine Carmody was probably right for you; she could always act love even if she didn't feel it. But I can't!" Hardly aware of what she had just said, she flung at him, finally, "Do you know how I feel? Trapped! And you don't care, because nothing except Las Viñas and Nadine Carmody ever touched you closely in your life."

She'd gone too far; she knew it as he took her shoulders and the dark eyes raged hotly close to her own. Some violent, primeval chemistry was working in them both, perhaps, for in spite of her pain and fury she felt herself swaying towards him, her face taut with hate.

135

The kiss, when it came, was ferocious and bruising. And it wasn't the only one. He kissed her throat and neck with the savage intensity of a man administering punishment, and when he let her go it was as if he had suddenly become conscious of the cruel dig of his fingers into the bare curve of her shoulder.

He was breathing heavily. His glance went all over her in a swift summing up. "God," he said under his breath. "Let's hope that's taught you something."

He turned and strode from the room. Sally slumped to the side of her bed and dropped her face into her hands. She had learned something all right: the magnitude of the hurt inflicted on him by Nadine Carmody.

*   *   *

It was those elderly Spanish relations who set the tone for the next few days, and after they had gone there seemed to be no reason to alter it. Sally had told herself that if Marcus resumed the slightly mocking, affectionate manner which had slipped so disastrously for a few minutes in her bedroom she would scream loud enough to be heard down in Naval Town. But there was no need to implement the threat. Marcus was cool and polite, ever thoughtful, but in no mood for mockery or any spurious display of affection. During Don Antonio's three days at Las Viñas the old man and Marcus drove round the estate and visited outlying farms. In the evenings there was a good deal of family talk, but Sally's lack of Spanish kept her free of it. On one of their evenings, indeed, she went down to the town with her mother for a few hours of sophisticated games and dancing. She won three pounds at mock-roulette, smoked half a dozen cigarettes and danced with several men who, to her own disgust with herself, all seemed uninterestingly alike. She returned to Las Viñas feeling old and despondent.

How would it all end? Was there anything at all that she herself could do to help matters? Sally couldn't think of a thing. It was impossible to confide in anyone. Her mother had always fought shy of complications and, in any case, would have been quite unsympathetic. To her the engagement was one of those magical pieces of good fortune for which Sally should be for ever grateful; Viola would never see it in any other way.

There was Carlos, of course. At the beginning, when it had seemed the deception need last only two or three weeks, Marcus had said they might take Carlos into their confidence. He was the old *señora's* doctor and able to judge just how much she could stand. But later Marcus had decided against the step, preferring to sound out his cousin; that was when he had learned that Doña Inez might never be in a condition to stand the shock of a broken engagement.

Still, Carlos was Sally's only hope. He was first a doctor, and as such would respect her confidence. She could put the whole thing to him, almost as a patient. Perhaps he even guessed a little already. She had caught him looking at her oddly once or twice; puzzled, questioning, solicitous because even though she was using more make-up there were tell-tale hollows under her eyes and a brittle brightness in her manner. Yes, if there was no other way out Sally would go to Carlos.

Ceremoniously, Don Antonio and the other three who had accompanied him were driven down to the harbor and seen aboard the steamer. Sally drove back with Marcus and Señor and Señora Suarez, and Doña Isabel informed her that the lilac was almost gathered, the presses full.

"Already ve talk of the *fiesta,*" she said. "Zis year is more egsitement because you vill be Lilac Queen. Two Saturdays from now. Is not, Marcus?"

A week and a half. Sally hoped her frock wouldn't arrive in time, but it did. In fact, four frocks and a suit were delivered to the house the very next day. Lovely frocks. The white gown, a crisp checked thing with a wide white collar, a slim-fitting flowery creation and a cocktail frock in vivid blue silk. The suit was of thin jersey, the straight jacket figured in lilac and white and the skirt plain lilac. It was beautiful, but what in the world had made her choose lilac? She was beginning to detest the stuff.

The weekend was quiet. Only Carlos came to dinner on Saturday, and Captain Northwick on Sunday. Viola was using her flair for sketching to plan the décor for a small amateur show the Navy were preparing, and she spent most of the weekend in her own balcony with sketching book and colored pencils.

As she told Sally, when she looked in on Sunday morning, "It's really most strange that there should be everything on this small island that I can possibly need. A nice pin-money job, lots of social life, a dramatic society that is short of someone artistic to plan the sets, and good continental cooking into the bargain."

"Not forgetting Captain Northwick of the impeccable manners and Mr. Essler of the middle-aged dreamy eyes," Sally reminded her. "And you're feeling very well, aren't you?"

"Better than I've felt for years. So you see, I wasn't such a fool to apply for that non-existent job in Barcelona!"

"You certainly weren't." Sally looked over her mother's balcony wall at the courtyard below, and asked casually, "Supposing things had developed differently. If Marcus hadn't become a potential son-in-law I'd now be working at the nursing home, and probably wishing I could complete my training. Would you have minded very much if I'd left you here and gone back to St. Alun's?"

"Of course I'd have minded, darling," said Viola, as she deftly shaded the background of her sketch. "But I don't think I'd have stopped you. I've so much here that I didn't seem to have in England, and though I might have missed you a bit, I wouldn't have put my feelings before your future. I don't think anyone could call me a possessive mother."

Sally didn't remind her of the last year or so in England. "I'm glad you've found a place where you feel you can be happy for a long time," she said, and left the matter there. Even within herself, Sally did not mull over the future; it was too painfully uncertain.

She went back to her own room and sat down at the writing table to answer a letter she'd had from her closest friend at St. Alun's, Betty Macey. She opened the wide central drawer, and at once noticed that Betty's letter, which should have been on top, had somehow pushed its way down to the bottom of the correspondence she kept there. Someone else must have rifled through the contents of the drawer and either displaced it or deliberately slipped it out of sight, after reading it.

Jarred, she sat back. Who in this house would want to read about Matron and Staffie and shenanigans in the nurses' hostel of St. Alun's? If they'd read one letter they'd probably read the lot, and much good might it do them! But why? What could anyone hope to learn from the feminine gossipy letters? And who could it be—the same person who had searched the room a couple of weeks ago?

She ought to do something about it, of course, but what? Nothing had emerged from the search, and this reading of her letters were almost too childish to bother about. It was just that it made her feel uneasy, as though she were being watched by someone hostile who suspected her position here at Las Viñas. Involuntarily, she remembered seeing one of the gardeners taking a long time over the tidying of the pool in the courtyard, and noticing that later he had paused while weeding the rockery below to speak with one of the maids. Surely there could be nothing suspicious about such countrified, ordinary islanders, particularly as they were employees here? But *someone* was unmistakably interested in Sally Sheppard, and whoever it was could easily bribe a gardener, a maid . . .

Oh, what nonsense. As if they'd jeopardize their livelihood in that way! She had only to complain to Marcus and the whole thing would be investigated. Perhaps, an insidious voice whispered, whoever it was knew just how precarious her relationship with Marcus had been, and still was. Perhaps they were smugly aware that she had no wish to approach him on a personal matter.

Sally had to leave her letter-writing for another day. She changed her shoes and went for a long walk.

Next morning she came abruptly awake at dawn. At first she hardly knew whether it was a sound or a nightmare that had jerked her back into consciousness, but after a few alarmed seconds it came again—the rattle of a pebble into had jerked her back into consciousness, but after a few alarmed sceonds it came again—the rattle of pebble into the balcony. She dragged on her dressing gown and went out into the cool misty grey light, looked over the wall.

Josef Carvallo stood below, staring upwards with an agonized expression on his white face. He wore an old corduroy suit and a white shirt which looked as though he had slept in them.

"*Señorita!*" he exclaimed in a loud whisper. "I need your help. Please dress and come down at once."

"What is it?"

"I cannot shout it here, but you are a nurse, and it is as a nurse that I need you. That is all. Please come!"

"Are you hurt?"

"Not I. It is someone else."

"Have you been to Carlos?"

"No, I cannot do that. I beg of you to come. This man has lost much blood . . . I will explain all as we go.

Sally was about to turn away; she waited a moment and asked, "Where is he?"

"At my cottage. There is no risk, *señorita*. I waited till it was light before waking you. You will come?"

"I'll come down, anyway."

Hardly aware of what she was doing, Sally slipped on a frock and a pair of walking shoes. Hurriedly she combed back her hair and dabbed a spot of eau de cologne on her face. Almost automatically, she went into the bathroom and collected scissors, dressings, cotton wool and iodine, after which she hastened noiselessly downstairs, unlocked the door and stepped out into the brightening dawn.

Josef was standing close to a tree, but as she appeared he came to greet her. His black curly hair was rough and bright with morning mist and his dark eyes were anxious and pleading.

"I am so glad you would come. I have no car, but it would not be wise for you to borrow one here; the servants must be stirring and they would hear."

She was walking as quickly as he, towards the gate. "Why is this a secret?" she asked. "Who is hurt?"

"I do not know him. He roused me last night—or rather it was early this morning. He banged at my door, and I found him fainting, with a torn shoulder. At first I did not want to let him in, but the man was so weak he could do no harm. I gave him my bed, bound up the shoulder in an old shirt and would have gone for Carlos. But this man would not let me do that. No doctor, he said. I must attend to the wound myself."

"But how extraordinary. Is he an islander?"

"I think not. His Spanish is unfamiliar."

"Then shouldn't you let the police deal with him? Even on San Palos there are a few policemen."

Josef shrugged, ran a hand over the short hair which now covered his own wound. "All I wish is to get rid of him, without trouble. In my life," with a hint of his roguish smile showing through his worry, "I have had enough problems of my own; other men's anxieties do not attract me at all. Please, *señorita,* I ask you to dress this man's shoulder so that I can send him away."

"I still think," she told him firmly, "that whether the man wanted it or not you should have called Carlos. If he's lost lots of blood he may be desperately ill, and the longer you keep him out of hospital the less chance there is of his recovery."

"I think," replied Josef with a grimace, "that this one is a strong man. He will certainly survive, and all I wish is to have him go from my house and leave no trace. I have told him I will give him food and get the wound dressed.

"Well, that's sensible, anyway. Is this really the way to your house?"

"It is the quick way, avoiding the road."

"Because you don't want to be seen?"

"Because I am in a hurry," he said. "I want this man away before the woman comes to clean my place."

They were walking quickly between pergolas of vines, Josef just ahead, pushing tendrils out of the way and looking back every few seconds to see that she was able to keep up. There seemed to be miles of cool green leaves and cascades of minute green grapes, but eventually they came out on to a rocky hillside, clambered over masses of orange and blue and white daisies and began the descent towards the coast road.

The sea, in the increasing light, looked calm and pewter-grey, lipped with white; the beach was a crescent of gold bordering the green countryside. Josef's house was lodged on the hillside, just above the rough road. It was of white stucco and curly pink tiles, and at one side it had an extensive *patio* which, she believed, Josef intended using as a workyard.

He opened an old black door and stood aside for her to enter. The tiled floors were bare, the furniture sparse in the room into which he led her. There was a table, a couple of chairs, a scarred old dresser and a single bed. And on the bed lay a man of something under forty, a heavily-built man in a tweed suit which looked incongruous with the roughly bandaged shoulder. Josef hadn't even taken off the coat.

Sally put down the things she had been carrying, bent over the man. He was pale and clammy, good-looking, in a square-faced fashion, but horribly blank about the eyes as he stared up at her.

He said something she didn't understand, and Josef answered him. In reply to Sally's query, Josef stated, "He said you must be quick."

"He said more than that."

"It . . . it wasn't complimentary."

"Who does he think he is? Get water, Josef."

Together they peeled off the bundle of temporary dressing and the tweed jacket. Sally cut away the man's own shirt and revealed a deep wide gash in the upper arm just below the shoulder. When she swabbed the wound the man grunted with pain, but again he apparently adjured Josef to hurry. Josef looked frightened, but Sally did not quicken her movements. She used iodine on a ball of cotton wool, heard the gasp of pain and saw a glazed look come into those dark eyes.

"I'm taking no responsibility, Josef," she said, a little unsteadily, as she prepared a thick gauze dressing. "He needs a doctor, and the best thing you can do it to get someone to take him up to the nursing home. Then he'll be off your hands."

"He will have no doctor," said Josef. "That is not such a bad wound. My own spilled more blood."

"You didn't get it the way he got his," murmured Sally. "He's been shot, and in England it's necessary to inform the police in such a case."

The word "police" must have got through to the man on the bed. He struggled upright, looked at them both and said something to Josef. Josef came forward and dropped the tweed jacket over the man's shoulders, covering most of the dressing, though a whiteness was visible through the ragged hole. The shoulder of the jacket was dark with blood and there were a few smears on the unshaven chin.

He stood up, a well-built man with grey-streaked hair and hard square features. Swaying slightly, he passed them both, went into the hall and out of the house. Sally stared at Josef, swung about as though to follow, but Josef caught her arm.

"Please, no," he said quickly. "Let him go. You are just one, and a woman. We have no weapons and he may be dangerous."

"But it's monstrous! He woke you up and you gave him your bed. He sent you out to get me and treated me as if I were a machine he'd switched on to do some small job. When he sent you for me you should have gone to the police!"

"He threatened me," said Josef with a helpless shrug. "Already I am fighting for this chance to start a business on the island, and trouble of that kind would ruin everything. Marcus has told me that if I am again in a brawl or seek that kind of companion, he will take the house for someone else."

"Well, there's one thing," said Sally. "San Palos is an island, and with a shoulder like that he'll have an awful job to get away from it."

But as she finished speaking there came a distant roar of a motor. She ran to the window, saw a launch arrowing away from the beach at full speed.

"Is that a naval launch? Did you know he had it there?"

"No. It must have been hidden by the trees." Josef sighed. "That was not my idea of a good way to spend the night."

"Do you know anything about him?"

"Nothing at all."

"Has anything like this ever happened before on the island?"

"I do not know—only that it has not happened to me. You are worn, *señorita?* I will make some coffee."

"No. I can't stay."

"But please," he said urgently. "I wish us to understand each other about this. I was anxious to help the man because he was hurt, but I could not risk people knowing he was here. That was why I came to you. I felt I could trust you to keep the secret."

"We don't have to protect a man of that kind," she protested. "It wasn't your fault he came here—just your bad luck. They've been enquiring about the borrowing of naval launches, and if we told about this man it might give them a clue."

"They have plenty of clues; they even know the name of the islander who helped to steal the launch." He shrugged and gave her a tired, little boy's smile. "I want nothing to do with it. The man has gone, *gracias a Dios,* and we can forget him."

"Do you have any notion about what he was?"

"He may have smuggled a little something on to the island."

"He didn't look like a smuggler."

"No headcloth and gilt earrings," Josef said dispiritedly, "but today they are less spectacular. Please say nothing to anyone about this."

"I can't promise that. If I hear another naval launch has been stolen I'll have to say something."

"At the risk of compromising yourself?"

She turned her head and looked at him, wide-eyed. "There's nothing compromising about dressing a wound. What are you getting at?"

"You are here alone with me," he said moodily. "Marcus would not like that. Now that you are officially engaged he would throw me out. I would be blamed, not you."

That wasn't true, and Josef knew it. But he was thinking only of his own skin. "I won't speak about it unless I have to," she said. "If I'd known it was a bullet wound I'd have given you the dressings and told Marcus."

"I had nothing here, and the man insisted on an antiseptic dressing. I could think only of you. You must know that I am sorry it should be necessary to ask another favor of you—your silence."

She moved to the door. "You're expecting a good deal, Josef."

"And I have no right; I know that. But you have so much, *señorita*. You have given up love, perhaps, but in its place you are gaining a great deal that may be worth more to you in the years to come. You have decided that marriage with Marcus, even on his terms . . ."

"I don't want to hear any more. It's quite light—I'm going now."

"I will accompany you," he said humbly. "Forgive me for speaking so plainly. I am more than a little in love with you—you must have guessed that."

He stood there looking rakish and depressed, and in spite of herself Sally felt a little ache of yearning, for she knew not what. *I am a little in love with you . . .* It sounded so sad that it hurt.

She drew a breath and said, "I daresay you've been a little in love a good many times, Josef. I'll make you a promise. If I ever feel I should tell someone about that man, I'll speak to you first—whether it's today, next week, or next month."

"Thank you," he said simply. "Thank you."

She turned from him then, waved him back and went on out into the morning light.

CHAPTER EIGHT

SALLY made a few casual enquiries, first of Carlos then of Captain Northwick. In effect, both said, "Yes, there's been a bit of bother, but you can be sure that the Navy and the police have things well in hand. They particularly wish the civilian population to know as little as possible. It's nothing serious." Which for the moment, was reassuring. She could relax and still keep her ears open.

Sunday was peculiarly quiet. No one but Carlos came to Las Viñas, and he stayed only fifteen minutes, with Doña Inez. Sally, her mother and Marcus lunched together in the courtyard. They separated and came together again at four-thirty for tea. They talked into the dusk, went in to change and met once more in the *sala,* for a short drink before dinner. Viola was half gay, half preoccupied. In a few short weeks she had so filled her life with things she had always longed for that there was literally no room, at present, for much more.

But when they were having coffee after dinner, she said, "Marcus, I've been thinking about the party I want to give for you and Sally. I'm rather tied up during this week, but next Saturday I'm free. Will that do?"

"It's the day of the Lilac Fiesta. Naval Town usually comes up *en bloc* for a night of fun."

"That's what I thought. Sally will look blooming in that incredible white confection, you'll probably go Spanish in velvet slacks and a silk shirt and the music will already be provided. I did want to give a party down in town, but a sort of buffet effort here in the courtyard with plenty of colored lamps and a few guitars might be more enjoyable to the Navy types. After all," apologetically, "this party will be for *my* friends more than yours. They have so many of their own sort of binge that I thought they might find a slightly continental one here at Las Viñas—which most of them have never seen except from the road—might be more exciting."

"Sally will be expected at the *fiesta* at eight, and she'll have to stay till about nine-thirty or ten. I shall be there myself, of course."

"That's all right. Everything starts late here. I'll invite the guests for eight and they'll all have arrived by about a quarter to nine. We'll eat and drink and talk for an hour, and then you'll bring Sally. At the first dull patch I'll suggest we all go up to the *fiesta*. By then it won't really matter whether you and Sally come with us or not."

The idea was typical of Viola. She wanted to be different, but hadn't the means to carry out the desire. The whole arrangement was slapdash, but through others it would be tightened up and made presentable before next Saturday; and in the end it wouldn't cost her a penny.

"I think you should forget it," Sally said in flat tones. "Let the Naval Town have their *fiesta* unadulterated. There are only two big *fiestas* here in the course of a year and I'm sure the English enjoy them. Besides, a party would disturb the *señora*."

"This suggestion has its points," said Marcus. "Doña Inez might be happy to hear a little noise of that kind for an hour or two, and it's right that your English friends should be invited to a celebration of some kind. I'll see if I can tie it up for you, Viola."

"Thank you, Marcus dear. I knew you would." She yawned delicately. "I'm so sorry. Perhaps I ought to go to bed. There's some naval top brass arriving tomorrow on an inspection tour, and I have to decorate the foyer and dining room of the hotel, for a luncheon. Will you excuse me?"

It might have looked bad had Sally jumped up at once to accompany her mother, so she remained seated, a little tensely, until all sounds of Viola's exit had receded. Then she stood up.

"Quiet days often seem more tiring than others," she remarked, and took a tentative pace towards the door."

"I thought we needed a peaceful interlude," he said abruptly. "I'm afraid I'm getting fed up with having the house full at every meal."

"It's you who invite the people," she pointed out evenly. "The only person I've ever asked to stay is Carlos, and he was used to coming here often long before my time."

"He wasn't accustomed to sitting across the table from you and watching everything you do," said Marcus, in edged tones, "and he didn't accept invitations so readily."

Her pulses began to throb uncomfortably fast. "Very well, I won't ask him again. It'll be up to you."

"I notice you don't deny he's paying you a good deal of silent attention. Or isn't it so silent?"

Fright was a hard ball in her chest. She saw Marcus standing straight and tall near the fireplace, awaiting her reply, and knew that she had to say something. It was a banal, "I don't know what you mean."

"I think you do. Carlos may be a fairly cold-blooded doctor, but he's also an intuitive Spaniard. He's not likely to be deceived by a bright smile, and I don't doubt he's made it clear, subtly, of course, that he's ready to share your secret sorrow."

"That's a horrible thing to say—of Carlos and of me. We've never spoken about anything of the kind!"

"I hope not. And you hadn't better, either of you. Go to bed."

But the sting in his voice was rather too much for Sally. "You've been painfully pleasant all day," she said in strained tones. "Why are you suddenly like this?"

He gazed at her through narrowed lids, flicked ash from his cigarette without watching where it landed. "If you were even slightly mature you wouldn't have to ask that. We're alone for the first time since that night in your room, and your first impulse is to escape. It might help to quiet your fears if I tell you it will never happen again, never! In that respect you're safe from me."

"I'm . . . I'm glad."

His lips curled with a hint of malice. "That would please you, naturally. You couldn't even handle Peter the pianist. You're only drawn to Carlos because you know he has tremendous discretion and a sense of fitness, and would never be more than the sympathetic doctor friend.

148

It was cruel of me to send Josef away, wasn't it? You must have felt a bit like Juliet when he whispered things from the *patio* after midnight."

She controlled a sudden alarm. He was only harking back to that occasion which had disturbed Katarina, and which she thought he had forgotten. In a voice as cool as she could make it she said, "You realize, of course, that the engagement is as much of a farce as it ever was. For Doña Inez's sake I may have to remain engaged to you for a very long time, but it will end some day. It's too late now, but I know what my answer would have been if Doña Inez hadn't stampeded us into that little ceremony last Saturday." She lifted her head. "It would have been *no*, Marcus."

He gave her a long dark glance, pressed out his cigarette in an ashtray with unnecessary force. But almost carelessly he said, "Too bad you took so long to get to the point. As you say, it's a bit late for it now. I think you'd better go to bed. Goodnight."

She went upstairs on legs that felt weak, reached the landing and saw Katarina walking rather more quickly than was her wont towards the end bedroom. Had the *señora's* companion been down there, listening near the half-open door of the *sala*? Surely it was patent to every servant in the place that Don Marcus had tied himself to someone . . . anyone . . . because Doña Inez had expected it of him?

As Sally entered her room she saw another servant emerge from the room next door, and at once she wondered if this were the one who had pried into the writing table and combed through her belongings. That feeling of suspecting everyone was so foreign to her nature that inside the room she turned the key, and stood there trembling. Or was she trembling from some other cause? Sally didn't know. She only knew that somehow she must get out of this muddle.

She went for a walk after breakfast next morning, and when she got back there was the session with Doña Inez. A surprisingly bright *señora*, who had recollected a few anecdotes from her youth and intended recounting them.

Sally listened, smiling and nodding occasionally, and when the old lady tired she mentioned her walk and how the roses had looked. Her half-hour was nearly up when Marcus joined them.

With his usual tenderness— a tenderness Sally had to steel herself to watch—he bent and kissed the papery old cheek. He made the usual enquiries and listened to the thin tones before saying, with a smile.

"I'm afraid I must leave you for a few days, *madrecita.* I've had a telegram from Barcelona and I will have to go there. I've already booked out on the Majorca ferry, but I doubt whether I'll get through to Barcelona before tomorrow. I'll be back by Thursday at the latest."

The *señora* lifted one small bony shoulder. "If you must, my son. It is business?"

"Of a kind. Just something that must be dealt with at once."

"Your agent there cannot manage it?"

"No. I'll get through as quickly as I can."

"I know you will, *caro.* In any case, we shall have your little Sally as an insurance against your early return!"

"Yes, you will."

He kept the smile as he looked at Sally, but she saw, with a sense of dull shock, that there was no amusement or even pleasantness in his regard. His eyes were cold black stones.

A few minutes later they came out of the bedroom together and walked to the head of the staircase. There, as Sally turned to descend to the hall, Marcus said aloofly.

"I shall be leaving in about ten minutes. For the look of the thing you'd better go down to the boat with me. I promise you my secretary will be there!"

She murmured something and went down to the hall. The self-effacing secretary who came four days a week to Las Viñas was standing just outside the main door, with a briefcase under his arm. He bowed, said something conventional and stood at attention till Marcus appeared, carrying a weekend case. Together, the three went down the steps to the drive, got into a car with Marcus at the wheel, and started away.

There was no need for many words between them on the way down to the harbor. For the last half-mile Sally could see the rippling blue sea with its scattering of little boats, and part of Naval Bay, where a flagship was anchored; apparently the top brass had arrived. There were a few palms leaning towards the harbor, and then they were on the old stone waterfront and slowing quite close to the black steamer which made the return journey three or four times a week to Majorca.

After he had switched off, Marcus turned in his seat to address the secretary. "Take my place and drive the *señorita* back to Las Viñas," he said. "You can spend tomorrow with Don Pedro's accountant."

"*Si señor*. Here is your briefcase."

"I shan't need it. You'd better drive straight off."

The secretary got out of the car and stood politely waiting for Marcus to emerge. For him, probably, Marcus made the parting look normal. He bent towards Sally, without quite touching his cheek to hers, said curtly, "Don't be *too* relieved that I'm going. It shows." And then he got out of the car, took his small suitcase and strode up the gangway on to the deck of the steamer.

Sally did not look back as the secretary drove with great care away from the harbor. She *was* relieved, but there was a horrid emptiness alongside the relief. San Palos without Marcus was like an opera without pulsing music; it made no sense at all.

And yet, when lunch-time came and she was quite alone in the courtyard facing an appetizing salad, a bowl of fruit and a silver coffee pot, she felt her limbs and facial muscles relaxing. The sky had hazed and it was cooler, and she was aware that for the first time in weeks she could think clearly and sensibly. Not about her own problem, but about anything external that caught her attention.

She reflected that her mother was probably having a wonderful time at the hotel luncheon. Somehow Viola was inevitably invited to each function she decorated, and it was easy to see her, in the soft powder-blue suit and matching hat, looking an adorable thirty-five among the older naval men. Sally thought, a little tremulously, that her father wouldn|t really mind, if he knew. He'd been unselfish enough to want Viola's happiness above everything else.

And that was true love, thought Sally. Making someone else happy . . . or even wanting them happy, without being the cause of it oneself. Was that how she loved Marcus? It was a question she couldn't even think about without going tense again, and she was determined to stay relaxed, at least until Thursday.

She spent the afternoon roaming the house as she had never roamed it before. She looked into the empty bedrooms; primrose and white, apple-green and white, rose-pink and white . . . and what was Marcus's color scheme—crimson and white? She didn't attempt to find out. She peeped into an upstairs sitting room which was pale blue, gold and silver grey, with portraits in gilt frames staring down at the buhl table in the centre of the room.

Downstairs, she even looked into the vast kitchen, where copper utensils winked from white walls and cupboards were enormous and old-fashioned and painted a shiny black. Katarina was there alone, mixing something in a small bowl. Her yellow face creased into a faint smile.

"One did not expect you here, señorita. Is there something I can do for you?"

"No, thank you. I'm exploring. This is the very first time I've seen the kitchen."

"It is not like yours in England?"

"Not much. I used to bake quite often, at home."

"Here there is no need for that. Even if the cook were ill the others could manage." Katarina tested the white paste she had been stirring. With a casualness that seemed studied, she asked, "It will be how long before you marry, señorita?"

Sally answered her rather shortly. "I don't know, Katarina. There's no hurry."

152

"You must pardon me for putting so personal a question. I have been here many years and everything that happens matters to me very much."

"Have you ever been married, Katarina?"

The woman's eyes stabbed at her before the glance was lowered once more to the task in hand. "No, I have not," came the tight-lipped reply.

"I'm sorry I asked — really sorry," said Sally. "I thought you had, or I wouldn't have mentioned it."

"Because it is a disgrace not to have married?" demanded Katarina almost roughly.

"No, of course it isn't. But if you're sensitive about it you naturally don't want to be questoned." Sally smiled. "Some man's loss has been the *señora's* gain. She depends on you entirely."

"She has been very good to me," said Katarina off-handedly. "For the *señora* and Don Marcus I would do anything."

Sally anxious to slide away from the sore subject, smiled cheerfully. "You've a soft corner for Josef too. Maybe one day you'll even trust *me* a little, Katarina."

A sour smile, and they were back to normal. "You are young and pretty and promised to Don Marcus. You do not need the trust of Katarina, but I will always do my best for the wife of Don Marcus."

It was nearly six o'clock when Viola came back from town, weary and intoxicated with her own success. Sally helped her out of the blue suit and stood behind her as she sat at the dressing table, creaming her face. With soft hands, Sally massaged her mother's shoulders and the back of her neck, and as she did so she watched the cleansing process which was so much a ritual that Viola did not have to pause between the various phases.

Viola accepted the news of Marcus's brief absence with equanimity. "Do you both good, darling. An engagement may help a couple to put their relationship on a fairly intimate footing before marriage, but it can be a most wearing time. And you don't have an easy man in Marcus. I imagine he's torn between phlegmatic English behavior and that caged-in passion of the Spanish fiancé. Sometimes, he looks all Spanish, and you wonder who's going to get it in the neck. No doubt his secretary and others have to suffer for you."

"For me?"

"Well, you're not very responsive, and he can't very well get rough with you, can he?"

"You'd be surprised, thought Sally. "Marcus never yet tackled anything he couldn't handle." And without pause: "You've done too much today. I can tell by your neck muscles that you're feeling the strain."

"Yes, I'm tired, but it was good." She sighed pleasurably. "Your fingers are wonderful, Sally—that's much easier. Will you draw my bath, darling?"

"Yes, and you're to have a light supper in bed."

"Lovely. I adore being fussed. Will you mind dining downstairs alone?"

"Not a bit. I shall go to bed early and read a book. Got everything you want?"

They parted, and Sally, after mooning about for a while outdoors, came into the house and asked the first servant she saw to serve dinner as soon as possible—nothing elaborate, please.

In the *sala* she felt restless. The french window was wide, but the atmosphere seemed oppressive with something that had nothing to do with the weather. At Las Viñas she had got into the habit of taking a small light drink at this hour, but somehow she couldn't face drinking alone. And she hadn't any cigarettes down here; there was nothing at all to do while she waited for dinner. She didn't want music, and come to think of it, she didn't want anything to eat, nor did she want to go to bed.

She paced across the room and stared out into the dusk beyond the lighted cloisters. The air was cool and soft with a bouquet blended from all the blossoms of a mediterranean island; it reminded her that often of late she had craved a solitude which, now that it was hers, she would have evaded if she could. Only in company was it possible deliberately to keep one's emotions in their place. She felt again as if she

154

had to go out and walk, or the gathering turmoil inside her would . . .

She started violently. A figure had appeared quite close almost without sound.

"Josef! You scared me."

He was smiling debonairly, bowing with theatrical politeness. "I must apologize. I saw you here, and thought you would have heard the car. May I come in?"

"I'm not sure. There's no one here."

"No mother? Then I must have permission from Doña Inez before I can stay for dinner."

"I haven't invited you," she said, and was suddenly glad to realize that her world had slipped away from the frightening chasm it had been close to. "Did you know Marcus had gone away?"

"Yes, I knew, or I would not be here." He smiled again, and winked. "You see, I am very frank. That is why you must believe me when I tell you I expected to be invited to stay for dinner with you and your very beautiful mother. I did not know she would be out also."

"She isn't out. She's having supper in bed."

"Then we are almost correct."

"No, we're not. I don't think you should ever come here without being invited by Marcus."

He grimaced. "It was you I wished to see not Marcus." He came right into the room and turned about. "Do you like my new suit?"

"It's much neater than your usual scruffy outfit."

He winced. "You are trying to hurt my feelings but they are a long way down, under my very thick skin."

She ignored this. "Have you heard anything more about that man with the wound?"

"Nothing at all, and I hear they have missed no launches. He was probably a tourist fisherman, poaching."

"Do local fishermen carry guns to scare off poachers?"

"How literal you are. What does it matter why he came to San Palos? Me, all I care is that he should leave my house. I would not again open the door at night to a stranger, I can tell you!"

"Well, I think it was most peculiar."

"Peculiar, but unimportant." He shrugged and ostentatiously looked at his watch. "At this time, I like a little wine."

There came a rap at the door and a maid entered the room. She saw Josef and hesitated. "*Buenos tarde*, Don Josef. *Señorita*, I came to say dinner is served."

Josef said airly, "Make it dinner for two. We will get Katarina to come and sit in the room with us!"

Sally was cross. "Have your drink and go. Some wine for the *señora*, please, Carmelita."

Josef helped himself and the maid disappeared. His glance at Sally was amused. "You are foolish not to enjoy yourself while the overlord is away. Do you think he is not finding himself some entertainment tonight?"

"Finish your drink," she said sharply.

"So the idea makes you a little jealous? I had not thought to see those eyes afraid and angry. Your eyes are very unusual, *señorita*—a color we never see in Spain. I could love your eyes . . . and skin."

"I'm afraid you won't have the chance, Josef. I believe you'd been out on a binge before you came here!"

"A binge? Is that a party? No, there was no party. As it happens, I drank alone, a long toast to myself. Just one long drink. So I am perfectly sober."

She stared straight at him, saw that his perpetual smile was sly and not in the least foolish. He had dressed in his best, even to the gold watch and cuff-links; she hadn't seen those clothes before, so for Josef this was an occasion. Yet he said he'd been out alone.

"Why did you come here?" she asked.

"To see you. I made myself smart, walked into the town and had my drink and paid the hotel taxi to bring me here. He drained his glass and set it down. "We have things to talk about, you and I. You know already that I am in love with you."

"Josef, please!"

"You think it is ridiculous for one such as I to speak to the fiancée of Marcus in this way? He has money and the estate, but I have nothing. Is that what you think? Well, you are wrong. I have been promised money for my business—big money. I could give you a fine house and some jewels." His eyes flashed queerly. "And I could give you love, which Marcus will never give you!"

"Please go," she said shakily. "Get out, or I'll have to call the servants."

"You will not call servants—you are too unsure of yourself. And it is Marcus who is to blame for that, just as he is responsible for my own lack of a home and a business." He threw out his hands pleadingly. "I have not expressed myself well; I was too anxious that you should know how much I need you, too eager to know how you feel about me. But we will forget that for a moment, no?"

Immaculately though he was dressed, he had the little boy look again, an air of uncertainty and despondency. Perhaps he *was* a bit high; perhaps he'd been celebrating the acquisition of a patron who would finance his ceramics venture, and had come here to gloat because he could now do without help from Marcus. It was no use being angry with him.

She said quietly, "Do go away now. I'm glad everything is turning out well for you, and I'll be happy to hear about it some time. But please go."

He poured a little more wine, planted his feet wide apart. "Not yet, *cara mia*. Do you intend to be alone here every day while Marcus is amusing himself in Barcelona?"

"I wonder if you speak as offensively to anyone else?"

"I am not being offensive. You trust Marcus, do you not?"

She watched him take something from his pocket, felt her jaw muscles tighten. "What are you getting at? What's that you're waving?"

"You did not see the telegram Marcus received, of course. This is a copy of it. Yes, you may have it. I bought it for you."

"Bought it?"

"Everything has its price, *señorita*. Read it."

She smoothed the flimsy sheet, read the pencilled words uncomprehendingly and started to read them a second time. They became clear, sharp little swords that stabbed into her consciousness.

"Am at the Catalania Hotel Barcelona. Have run out on my contract because I love you. Longing to see you and meet your grandmother. Please come to me darling. Nadine."

"Nadine," Sally whispered.

"You and I know who she is," Josef said almost as softly. "It has started even before you are married. Can you bear to think of how it will be afterwards?"

Sally crumpled the paper tightly into her hand. "Leave me now, Josef. I'm begging you."

"But I cannot leave you so sad, *querida*. I did this for you—just for you—and at once you send me away! But I can help you . . ."

"You can't. No one can," she said bleakly. "Why did you do it—get a copy of the telegram?"

"I have told you—it cost money. You passed me in the town—you and Marcus and the clerk. I was curious, and from a distance I watched Marcus embark. I made enquiries, and heard he had received a business call to Barcelona." He pressed the tips of his fingers together and spoke with subdued excitement. "I thought much, and felt what they call a hunch. Had he received this call by telephone or telegram? I discovered there had been a telegram, and with money I bought a copy of it."

"Did you also have a hunch as to the sender?" she asked bitterly.

"No. I only hoped."

"Hoped!" She gazed at him, her eyes big and dark with pain. "You *hoped* it would be that woman?"

He nodded dejectedly. "For your sake, *niñacita*. It has come in time, has it not? It will save you a most unhappy marriage. I did not want to hurt you like this. I did not know you cared so much for Marcus."

She drew an unsteady breath. "You've done what you came to do, Josef. If you want dinner here you can have it alone. I'm going upstairs."

"But one moment." His urgent hand did not quite touch her arm. "I wish you to know that whatever you decide to do about this, I will help you if you need me. The other morning you were good enough to come to my cottage and help me get rid of that undesirable man, so there will be no obligation, *señorita,* no favors. I am in your debt and will be most grateful for an opportunity to assist you. You may be sure I will say nothing to anyone else." He seized her hand and kissed it, and when he lifted his head she saw his eyes were bright with what looked like tears. "I will embarrass you no longer, but do not forget that I am at your command!"

He slipped out the way he had come, and for a full minute Sally was unable to move. Then the maid knocked again at the door.

"I have spoken to Katarina, *señorita* . . ." She stopped. "Don Josef has gone?"

Sally nodded. "I think so. I have a headache, Carmelita. I shan't want any dinner. And tell Katarina not to worry. I'm going to bed."

On legs that felt flexible Sally went upstairs to her room. After several completely blank minutes she became aware of a tiny ball of thin paper in her hand, and with trembling fingers she half opened it. Not to read, though; never in her life would she forget those words. She struck a match, the thing flared and was gone in a black wisp which fluttered on to the carpet.

Just like that, she thought. But it was only paper that had vanished in smoke, not the reality.

CHAPTER NINE

IT was not till the small hours that shock began to fade into acceptance. Sally lay gazing at the rectangle of pale radiance beyond the balcony, and as resignation took possession she felt calmer. Perhaps a sense of relief would come next; she hoped so. It was making up your mind about something that hurt; once you'd come to a decision things got easier. She was already thinking more clearly.

Bitterly, too, though. Marcus in Barcelona with Nadine Carmody — if not tonight, then tomorrow night and perhaps the night after. He would be shatteringly cool towards her, no doubt about that. But he wouldn't be able to keep it up. No man could, against a woman he loved who had come halfway across the world to beg his forgiveness. Trying to think oneself into Marcus's personality was impossible, but Sally felt she did know enough about him to calculate just slightly how he had felt about that telegram, and how he would react.

He wouldn't have felt helpless for long, not Marcus. The first thing was to see Nadine and assure himself that, for him, she was willing to relinquish career and all that went with it. Then would come consideration for Doña Inez. Where she was concerned there could be nothing hurried or savoring of indiscretion; the matter would take time.

Finally, he had to deal with Sally Sheppard. And that was where Sally's thoughts became snarled up like a tangle of barbed wire. It wasn't in Marcus to go back on the engagement he had made official, but could he ever persuade himself to marry someone he didn't love? Wasn't it possible, because his code was strict, and his love for Doña Inez the most important and lasting thing in his life, that he would decide to go on with the marriage? And Nadine, the woman half scorned and totally rejected; how would he handle her? But here a niggling suspicion crept in, took shape in Sally's mind.

Nadine was an actress, had been clever enough in England to attract a New York theatre agent. Deep down, however much she wanted Marcus, she must also want to continue her career on the stage. He was in a position to promise her almost anything except marriage, and why shouldn't Nadine settle for that? A luxurious flat, enough capital to buy a share in some production calculated to make her famous, and a month now and then of his company. That was what Josef had meant, wasn't it? And Josef had known Marcus most of his life.

By now Sally's head was one vast ache, but she couldn't stop thinking. Marcus would come back looking suave and aloof, expecting to find everything as he had left it. Because of Doña Inez, nothing would change. But of course he hadn't bargained for Josef's interest in his trip to Barcelona, or for the wretched telegraphist who had sold a copy of the wire. What was a business visit to Barcelona? Nothing at all.

But one thing became very clear to Sally. As the only woman in Marcus's life she might have stood a chance. Propinquity, the sharing of small intimacies, a growing knowledge of each other—together they might have roused something in Marcus which was akin to love. And he would certainly be devoted to the woman he married. Devoted, sincere, considerate . . . but none of those qualities or even the sum of them amounted to love as Sally wanted it. She wanted something that was as simple and direct, as heart-warming and exciting as the dawn of a glorious summer's day. In lighter mood she might also have confessed that she wouldn't mind some electricity in the air occasionally!

So it had now become quite clear that she could never marry Marcus. Not that she had ever really accepted the possibility. It was just that she had now arrived at the certainty that it could never happen. Then what was the alternative? While she was here at Las Viñas the engagement couldn't peter out from malnutrition, and if she decided to leave the island there was the risk of collapse to Doña Inez. She was still trapped, unless . . .

It was really very obvious, but she had fought away from it till it had to be faced. If Marcus wanted Nadine as his wife he should have her. There was a way out of the situation, but only Sally could take it, and it would need such tremendous care that she daren't attack it until she was thoroughly rested and sure of herself. Not tomorrow—today, that was—but on Wednesday. By then she would be entirely calm and perhaps even relieved that the end of it all was near.

Sally turned her pillow for coolness, buried her face in it and let the tears run out. Eventually she dozed, and when next she awoke it was to face the sanity of morning light.

It was a blue, serene day. Viola went down to the store, and Doña Inez accomplished her dozen short paces along the corridor and back to her room. As she told Sally, over a cup of chocolate at eleven,

"When one is old small things make up the enjoyment of daily life. One's favorite omelet for lunch, a chapter read from a cherished book, the sight of a bird seen only on San Palos, the convent bell when the wind is right—and for me, that short walk outside the room. This is what they call second childhood—the magnifying of simple things. It is in the middle years—from twenty to sixty—that one needs fire and thunder."

"Some people settle for less before they're sixty," said Sally with a smile. "May I read that chapter from your cherished book?"

"It is in Spanish, but there is an English book I like also. A peculiar story which, not being English, I shall never understand. 'The Vicar of Wakefield'."

Sally read, and in a little while became beguiled and amused herself. She left Doña Inez nodding among her pillows and took a more modern book out to the courtyard, where the old Sealyham slept away his days. When Carlos arrived he gave her his usual courteous salute and went into the house. Within ten minutes he was back again, pausing beside Sally's chair.

"So you are quite alone today. Would you care to go with me to my brother's house for lunch? Isabel would be happy to see you."

"Thank you, but I don't think so, Carlos. My mother may be back for lunch."

"With her car? Perhaps both of you would join us there when she comes?"

"Mother's always a little tired after the morning at the store," said Sally hastily.

"And my sister-in-law is not easy for Señora Sheppard to understand?" He smiled. "Isabel likes you, Sally. She is fuming against the slowness of this week, because she wants to see you so much at the *fiesta*."

"She's very sweet. If I laugh at the way she speaks English it's because I enjoy it. She's one up on me, anyway; I can't talk Spanish."

"But you will learn. Doña Inez was telling me that you read to her this morning."

She nodded. "I sent her to sleep. How is she today?"

"Remarkably well. As it is now so warm, I have given permission for a small day-room to be prepared for her downstairs. She may use it when she is in the mood."

"I'm so glad." Sally hesitated before asking idly, "Do you think she's quite recovered from that stroke, or whatever it was?"

"The condition is still there—the cause of the attack. But she is as well as I have known her during the past few years."

"Is her heart good?"

"For her age, excellent."

"Which means it's a bit tired?"

"Yes. With care she may last for several years."

"Then she's in far better shape than when I first came here?"

He was looking down at her as she sat near the wrought-iron table, and the fact that he thought her questions a little odd was audible in his voice. "You have brought comfort and security to the *señora*. Why do you wish to know this, Sally?"

She answered quickly, without looking up. "I'm interested, naturally. We've taken care that nothing in the least controversial shall reach Doña Inez, and I wanted to know whether such precautions are still necessary. She seems so very alert and understanding that I wondered if she could stand rather more than we think. What's your opinion?"

He shrugged, characteristically. "Be honest with her as far as you feel it is wise, that is all. You have seen her daily for some time, and I am sure you are by now aware if there is worry or even a slight uneasiness in the *señora*. While there is no sign of this uneasiness you may say what you please in her presence. I feel you already knew that."

"Yes, I did. But you've put it plainly for me, Carlos. Thank you."

He lingered, as though he would have liked to say more. But Sally didn't look straight up at him, and after a bit he gave his small bow and departed.

Viola came for lunch and went to bed after it. Later she told Sally she had been invited to Mr. Essler's villa for the evening. A dinner party for eight. He was very charming —didn't Sally think so? His villa was sure to be furnished in the best possible taste, which was rather more than one could say of Captain Northwick's cottage. Really, the Captain was hopeless!

For Sally, the evening was long and very quiet. Once, in her room, she listened, and thought it was like the long minutes of stillness before a storm. A few rustlings outside, the discreet murmur of servants below in the dark *patio*. and then a deeper silence which would not be broken till midnight, when a car brought her mother to the foot of the steps. Sally got into bed at eleven, and perhaps because she had made her decision, however painful, she slept.

It was about ten-thirty next morning when she tapped gently at the door of the *señora's* room. Doña Inez was sitting in her padded mahogany wheelchair and was close to the balcony. She waved Katarina away.

"Chocolate at eleven, Katarina. Maria may bring it in. Go out for an hour if you wish."

Katarina frowned, but obeyed. Sally, seated half facing the old *señora*, turned her head and looked out towards the climbing roses. The full-blown blossoms had been snipped off and new buds had appeared, some of them already bursting from fat green sheaths. A cloud of gnats hovered above the balcony rail, and moved off downwards.

Doña Inez allowed her sharp little glance to travel over Sally's fair head and down to her shoulders. "That is one of the dresses from Barcelona? It is pretty, on you. You must order more of them."

"There are some more on the way. Would you like me to read to you again?"

"I have no wish to sleep yet! Tell me what you do with yourself while Marcus is away."

This wasn't quite the sort of opening Sally needed. She answered, "I'm afraid I'm being lazy, but I may go down to the nursing home this afternoon."

"You still wish you could work there?"

"I did enjoy nursing," Sally said, as though casually stating a fact. "But I've never really wanted to be just a nursing assistant. I used to be terribly determined to get through my training, and I still hanker for it a little."

The *señora's* expression softened. It is because you are young and active, and at the moment there is not much for you to do here. When you are married you will feel differently. I am sure you know that Marcus will be an exacting husband."

Sally nodded, while she searched for words. "You want his marriage very much, don't you?"

"Of course."

"All you wanted to hear, when he returned from England, was that he had brought a fiancée?"

"Yes, that is true." The bony little face looked thoughtful. "He is the only del Moscado—I no longer count. He must marry."

Sally moistened a dry lower lip, but managed a lightness in her tones. "So it didn't really matter very much whom he'd chosen, did it?"

"I trust his good taste," said Doña Inez dryly. "I will not pretend that I would not have preferred that he choose a girl brought up in the Spanish way—someone who was educated for marriage to a man of his standing and not taught to earn her living—but his own feelings were more important. It is imperative that Marcus should marry a woman he loves." She slanted another of the eagle glances at the pale young face that was slightly turned from her. "You must not expect too much of an old woman. The only love I have left is love of family, and to me that means Marcus and his wife."

"I realize that."

"What you are asking," said Doñna Ineza shrewdly, "is whether I could ever have loved someone like you for yourself. Is it not so?"

"Perhaps."

"Then please forget it. When you marry Marcus you will become part of him, and for me that is enough."

It was half an answer, a rather painful half. But Sally had to know the rest. For the moment, though, she thought it best to remain quiet, while Doña Inez relaxed. Not that the old *señora* had become in the least anxious. On the contrary, she had looked keen-eyed and interested. And it was she who broke the short silence.

"It is because you are young and away from your own country that you feel insecure. And it is because Marcus did not take you with him to Barcelona that you are asking yourself whether he has enough feeling for you."

"I'm not wondering that," said Sally at once. "I was only curious to hear how you feel about . . . about me personally." She gave a brief laugh which she hoped sounded less brittle to the *señora* than it did to herself. "Just as a point for discussion, *señora*—supposing Marcus's fiancée had turned out to be someone quite different? Supposing she were a dress designer or a journalist . . . or

166

an actress? Would it have made any difference to your own feelings?"

"None," said Doña Inez firmly. "To me, it is only important that there *is* a fiancée. I think you wish me to be quite honest, do you not?"

Sally nodded. A sort of fright seemed to have paralyzed her throat muscles. Doña Inez gave her another long penetrating glance, sighed and said,

"Be content, *cara mia*. You are a sweet girl and you will be a loyal wife. Later you will have maturity and the power to make Marcus adore you. Until then you must be happy with as much affection from him as you can inspire. You understand?"

"Yes," said Sally in a thread of a voice. "I understand."

She understood so well that the pain was a probe, needling into her heart. She had asked for a little, just enough to make quite certain that Sally Sheppard, as a person, could never harm Doña Inez. But, gently and ruthlessly, she had been given the whole works. Not only was she dispensable, so long as another fiancée were there to take her place, but it was also known—to Doña Inez at least— that Marcus was not in love with her!

She tried to pull her shattered thoughts together. There sat the old Spanish woman, tranquil, with the tiny smile upon her patrician features. What had she felt—that she was giving sound advice to a young woman about to tie herself to the del Moscado Durant family? And what had she imagined—that Sally would be content without love because she would be gaining so many material things?

Sally would rather her thoughts had remained in splinters. The thing didn't bear thinking about.

Somehow she stayed on till Maria brought the chocolate. But the cloying smell of the stuff was too much for her. She pleaded a slight headache and said she would go down and get rid of it in the garden. As she left the *señora* she avoided meeting those wise old eyes; she had to.

* * *

Doña Isabel came to view the *fiesta* gown that afternoon. She sat in Sally's bedroom and crooned her delight, came downstairs and had tea, still praising the "mos' lofly zing in ze vorld." In her old chauffeur-driven car she took Sally to the *fiesta* ground, where marquees were already flaunting their striped roofs and scalloped awnings, and islanders worked upon the wooden structure for the lilac bower. The smell from the presses, a quarter of a mile away, was too concentrated to be sickly. In fact, it hardly reminded one of lilac at all.

The donkeys were out to grass again, and several of them wandered cheerfully among the sideshow tents. Ranged close to the road stood cartloads of tarpaulins and other gear, and in groups on the grass women were sewing gay flags and painting straw hats they had made earlier. There was laughter and gossip, an air of anticipation and zest. Someone lit a jumping cracker and was good-humoredly chased. A tenor soulfully tested his low notes and a woman threw him a flower.

Feeling thoroughly out of place, Sally was glad when Doña Isabel suggested it was now time to leave; she always cooked dinner herself and tonight it must not be late because Carlos was coming, as well as Sally. So much for her stupid efforts to keep away from the doctor, thought Sally. As if it mattered.

There were just the four of them that evening, and Doña Isabel was jubilant about the success of her *pastas* and *trasajo,* heavy dishes that Sally tackled as bravely as she was able. But the coffee was excellent, and taking the risk of shocking Doña Isabel, Sally accepted a cigarette from Carlos and let him light it. She lay back in an easy chair, smiled dutifully whenever she met the other woman's glance, and let the men do the talking. Seeing that this was the custom in this house, she could withdraw in thought while appearing to be present. Not that she wanted to be alone with herself. What she wanted was the impossible; to fade right out and be nothing at all.

Between nine-thirty and ten Carlos said about six times that he must leave, and each time he was smiled at and drawn once more into discussion. Carlos was a gentle man, but Pedro was even gentler; he was entirely without envy or dislike, and very willing to think the best even of people whom Carlos shrugged off. You got the impression that Pedro regarded his brother as headstrong, self-assertive and dogmatic, a man who would mellow with age. It was rather touching.

At last Carlos got up. "The evening has been so pleasant that I would prefer to stay, but I still have to see a patient at the hospital. I will drive Sally home."

"Unless she would care to stay with us for another hour?" said Don Pedro courteously.

"Thank you, but no, *señor*. I think I must go too. You and Doña Isabel have been most kind, and I've enjoyed the evening immensely."

"*Mucho* sleep for *fiesta*, no?" beamed Doña Isabel. "Zis vill be our mos' zuccessful Fiesta of Lilacs!"

In her plump good nature she was overwhelming, but a dear. Sally touched a cheek to the one Doña Isabel offered, said goodnight and accompanied Carlos to his car. They drove away into a faintly lucent darkness.

Carlos said, "My brother and his wife feel honored each time you go to their house. They are both simple people."

"They're very sweet. I've never been to *your* house, Carlos; you don't seem to spend much time there yourself."

"For me the house is sleeping quarters and an office—not much more." His shoulders lifted. "I eat at the nursing home, with you and Marcus, with Pedro, with a patient here and there. It is a bad habit, you think?"

"Very bad. You should marry one of the nurses in the British section of the hospital." She saw him look at her quickly. "I was only joking, but is there someone?"

Carlos smiled, but his negative did not sound entirely convincing. "Do I look like a man in love?"

"Not terribly. How long have the British nurses been here?"

"For some time," he replied, almost offhandedly. And she said no more.

Sally could not prevent his getting out of the car when they reached Las Viñas, but she did place restraining fingers on his arm as he made to mount the steps with her.

169

"Please don't bother, Carlos. You still have work to do. It's been a lovely evening—and thank you for the lift."

"My pleasure. Goodnight, *señorita*."

Sally went up the steps into the light of the courtyard, turned, with her head still bent, towards the house. Then suddenly she was halted, and her head lifted sharply.

"Marcus!"

He seemed to be smiling, but in the darkness she wasn't sure. "I got a lift home too," he said, "with some of the Navy who'd been on leave and were coming back by their own plane. It's good to know you haven't been lonely."

"I've been out to dinner at the Suarez house—Don Pedro's."

"I imagined that. You're looking very lovely. How are you?"

"I'm . . . all right." She was walking with him into the house. "We went up to the *fiesta field* this afternoon, and Doña Isabel invited me to their place for dinner."

"If you're trying to tell me that you didn't know Carlos would be there, I believe it already. Come into the study and have a nightcap with me."

"It's rather late."

"Only eleven. You can tell me what you've been doing since Monday."

And would he reciprocate? Not that she'd dare ask him to. She wouldn't be able to speak to him about it, not yet. She didn't really want to know the details. She knew too much already.

She entered the study with him, and was glad that he switched on only one light, the lamp on the desk. Lowering herself into one of the armchairs, she asked, in a steady voice, "Did your business go well?"

"So-so." With a lift of the shoulders he dismissed it. "What will you have—a spot of gin?"

"No drink, thanks, but I'd like a cigarette."

He gave her one and lighted it, before setting the flame to his own. "Well, how have you been amusing yourself?"

"Quietly. Reading, mostly."

"No visitors?"

She shook her head and saw a change in his face; a dilation of the nostrils, a narrowing of the lids. Offhandedly she said, "I suppose you've heard that Josef came here on Monday evening. He had a drink, and left."

"That's not true," he said curtly. "He had dinner here. Katarina told me."

"Did he?" She flickered a glance across at him. "I wasn't aware of that. While I was here he had one drink . . . no, two. I didn't want anything to eat. He went out to the veranda and I naturally thought he was leaving Las Viñas. I went straight up to bed."

"Josef came because he knew I was away, didn't he?"

"So he said."

"And what was the other reason?"

Sally wasn't prepared to answer that. Almost unconsciously she had come to the conclusion that nothing could be done about her own problems till Sunday. She owed that much to Doña Isabel Suarez. With the *fiesta* past she would be free to act in her own interests. Early on Sunday morning she would tell her mother she couldn't marry Marcus. And then, as soon as she could see him alone, she would tell Marcus himself.

She tapped ash into a tray he had placed nearby. "Josef doesn't like you, Marcus."

"I've known that for years."

"Well, that's why he came while you were away."

"That was easy to guess."

His cigarette had gone out and he put another between his lips. She saw the faintly bitter pull at his mouth as he jutted the cigarette to his lighter, the brief, fed-up glance he gave her as he blew smoke through his nostrils and dropped the lighter into his pocket. She sat without speaking, a little taut, with her legs extended and her head back, so that the slender throat looked vulnerable.

He said abruptly, "Josef will be leaving San Palos shortly. I doubt whether he'll come back again."

"He didn't know that on Monday. He looked most prosperous—said someone had offered to finance his ceramics."

"He'll have to start his factory elsewhere. I'm giving the house to one of our own workers." With a vicious flick of his fingers he added, "That little house used to be quite a show place; you should see it now."

Perhaps it was her very silence that gave Sally away. It was a frantic kind of silence, as though her mind were desperately casting round for something, anything she might mention to get past that moment. But her expression must have revealed that she had seen Josef's cottage. Marcus looked at her queerly and stood up. He jabbed out the new cigarette and walked to the window. Looking out into the night he said tightly,

"I'm not going to row with you; I'm certainly not in the mood to keep a quarrel within bounds. A plain warning wouldn't be any good; I can tell that from the way you looked at me when we met out there in the *patio*. So I'm afraid I shall have to be autocratic. I forbid you to leave this house before the *fiesta* on Saturday. I'll take you up there myself."

Sally's lips quivered. She pushed herself up out of the chair. "I doubt whether I shall want to go out. But if I did, Marcus, I wouldn't ask you first. Goodnight."

* * *

Once more, during the next couple of days, Sally marvelled a little wearily at the man who was Marcus Durant. He hardly left Las Viñas at all, but there were guests for lunch and dinner, convivial evenings, a quietly entertaining teaparty in the small rest-room which had been prepared downstairs for Doña Inez, and a gay *pequeña-fiesta* for the children of the lilac farmers and laborers in the grounds of Las Viñas. Every day he was the smiling host, the charming and considerate master of the estate. And every day he saw to it, unobtrusively, that Sally was never alone. She became quite certain that she couldn't possibly have left Las Viñas without being followed. It was archaic and fantastic. Marcus didn't want her, but he considered himself stuck with her. He imagined her sloping off for an hour with Josef, tainting the marvellous name of Durant merely by implication. Marcus could go off for days to Barcelona with his lady-love, but Sally must remain a prisoner on the island, and even a prisoner in the house so long as Josef Carvallo remained on San Palos. It was quite incredible, yet it was happening.

And as a background to it all there was the *fiesta* spirit, the dropping in of friends, talk of the increased price this year for the lilac concentrate, and conjectures about the grape harvest. Only Viola showed any despondency, and that just once in private. Sally had taken a fresh box of tissues to her mother's room, and Viola, emerging from the bathroom, had thanked her, and then sighed.

"It's a pretty idea—celebrating a good haul of lilac—but it does seem ridiculous that it should displace everything else. I hope you're not terribly disappointed."

"About what?"

"Darling, really! Our party, of course. I think you should have stood out against Marcus in this instance. I've a right to give a party for you, and if I happen to choose the *fiesta* weekend it's no one's busines but my own. My friends are nearly all English, and I don't see that the beastly carnival should be allowed to interfere with my plans. Tomorrow I have to tell everyone that it's off."

"You mean there'll be no party here on Saturday?"

Viola looked puzzled. "Didn't you know Marcus had vetoed it?"

"No. No, I didn't."

"He told me this afternoon, and I naturally thought you'd decided it between you. He said there'll be enough going on here this weekend, and asked me to postpone my little effort for a while. As this happens to be his house I've no option but to give in. He said something about wanting to give the servants the evening off so that they could enjoy the dancing, but I felt there was more to it than that." Viola sat down in front of the dressing-table mirror, gave herself a troubled look and added, "I know I'm not much of a mother, darling, but I do feel I should warn you that life isn't going to be easy with Marcus; it was all too good to be true. Under that urbane charm of his there lurks a devil, and if I were you . . ."

Sally didn't wait to hear the advice. She patted her mother's shoulder and said, "We'll have a long talk after the *fiesta*—perhaps on Sunday morning while you're relaxing in bed. Cheer up now and make yourself ravishing —you'll have both the swains here for dinner tonight!"

In her own room, as she changed, Sally hardly thought about the cancelled party. It was only another indication of Marcus's attitude since the telegram had arrived from Nadine Carmody. Such a party, given by Viola, would set another external seal upon the engagement, and that was something Marcus was in no frame of mind to tolerate. He was marking time, as Sally was. But she felt he didn't intend to act so soon as she did. He was waiting for something—perhaps some word from Nadine.

Saturday came, the morning threaded with excitement, the afternoon quiet at Las Viñas but lively with anticipation at the *fiesta* ground. No guests today, and Viola had a little huffily accepted an invitation to spend the whole day with the Navy crowd, so that the quiet was all-pervading and slightly ominous.

In the late afternoon a huge box of lilac blooms was delivered, and unexpectedly, it was Katarina who offered her services to Sally as a dresser. The Spanish woman took tremendous care and lamented several times that the pins would ruin the material. But when Katarina had finished, even Sally had to admit the effect was dazzling.

The white gown, with its fitted strapless bodice and floor-length flowing skirt, was a magnificent ground for the long rich sprays of pastel-tinted lilac. A single spray crossed the bodice, and several had been secured to the skirt slantwise, so that in artificial light, at a distance, it would look as though the material were magnificently embossed. With the flowers had come a tiara made of florets from the tips of many sprays. Clipped close to the crown of her head, with the pale hair softly waving, it was the prettiest headdress Sally had ever seen.

Katarina stood back, her hands clasped. "It is nearly time that you go. Please . . . stay just there, like that. I will call Don Marcus."

Sally moved quickly. "No, don't! You've made a marvellous job of it, Katarina. Are you going to the *fiesta?*"

The woman's usual rather blank expression came back to her face, and her lids lowered. "I have nothing to celebrate, *señorita*. No lilacs . . . no engagement. For you, I wish much happiness—you must believe that."

"Of course I believe it. Please don't look so sad."

"I feel sad," said the woman simply.

But she had turned with her usual sangfroid towards the door when there came a light tap on the panel. Katarina turned the handle, and stood back as Marcus entered the room. Sally stiffened and took care to avert her glance.

Katarina said quietly, "The *señorita* is *bellissima, no, señor?* Like a bride."

Marcus nodded, his smile set. *"Bellissima* is the only word, Katarina." And to Sally: "You don't need the necklace, but the crowd likes to see some jewels. Give it to me and I'll fasten it for you."

She felt Marcus's hands touch her bare shoulders lightly, a faint warm breath across her cheek as his lips brushed her hair. He was playing to Katarina, so that she would have a good bedtime story for Doña Inez.

Feeling too choked even to fabricate a smile, Sally accepted the mink stole which had accompanied the second batch of frocks from Barcelona and preceded Marcus from the room.

CHAPTER TEN

ON San Palos the Lilac Fiesta was recognized as the start of the summer season. It had an air of unrestrained gaiety but there was an almost gentle atmosphere about it compared with the rumbustious clamor of the Carnival of the Grapes which marked summer's end. Not that any of the usual signs of *fiesta* were absent. There were the huge *papier-mâché* figures nodding on poles, grotesquely dressed clowns doing acrobatics, lovely *señoritas* in gay dress, masked men in velvet slacks and white silk shirts, and all the sideshows and food stalls, toy vendors and music-makers that could possibly be packed into five acres of pastureland. But in place of an abundance of wine and grapes, there was the plenitude of lilacs; and instead of the grilling heat of a late summer night there was the refreshing zephyr of ageing spring.

Marcus and Sally arrived at the field exactly five minutes to eight. They were met by Doña Isabel, who recovered from her ecstasies over the gown in time to escort Sally to the immense arbor of lilacs which had been prepared for her appearance at eight o'clock. Marcus remained near the car. He lit a cigarette and leaned back against the bonnet, watching Sally disappear into the mountain of lilacs. This was the back of the bower. She would go up half a dozen wooden steps and emerge on to the platform where her coracle-shaped throne was ready to receive her.

The custom of installing a queen for the Lilac Fiesta had never before struck him as childish. In fact, it had always been his privilege to escort whoever it was down from the bower and beg the first dance, and he'd rather enjoyed it. The islanders loved it, bless their romantic hearts. The trouble was, he felt out of tune with the whole business this year.

Crowds were clustered about the tower of lilacs. He could see their upturned faces, tanned and shining, the girls red-lipped and smiling their expectancy. Then the concerted, long-drawn "A . . . ah!" as Sally appeared and took her place. Thunderous clapping and shouts of *"Olé"* and the time-worn *"Bellissima!"* They caught the little gifts Isabel had asked Sally to throw, cried their thanks and tossed flowers up to her; rosebuds, chiefly. A compliment because she was English.

Marcus ground out his cigarette, knew he should go forward and see how she looked up there in her billowing frame of lilac. Instead he turned away and strolled in the semi-darkness halfway round the field. Two men who had started their *fiesta* rather early were bickering amiably over a jar of wine. He'd promised Pedro he'd make sure the police were on duty. They weren't really necessary, but Pedro felt their presence an insurance against failure.

Marcus found the official tent, guarded by a solitary policeman, who saluted him smartly.

"You have seen Don Pedro?" he asked him in Spanish.

"No, Don Marcus."

"It doesn't matter. I'll tell him you're on duty. How many of you, by the way?"

The man lowered his voice. "Only three, *señor*. We are all that could be spared. The others are on special duty."

Marcus smiled. "Special? Is there a dance on in Naval Town?"

The man looked sheepish. "I do not know much about it, *señor*, but our police are co-operating with the authorities in Naval Town. They believe that those people will take advantage of the *fiesta*. The *señor* knows what I mean?"

"Yes, I know. It's very wise to keep the police down there. I shall be somewhere around, if you need any help. Blow your whistle."

"Thank you, *señor*."

Marcus walked on. The noise was unbelievable, the blare of accordion music excruciating. On the dance floor, which was almost in the centre of the field, figures were whirling and strutting while onlookers clicked castanets and sang, ate *pastas* and sweetmeats and exhorted the musicians to greater efforts. The striped marquees bulged, and a perpetual crowd moved very slowly past the Lilac Queen, looking up, smiling and waving. At a distance of about a hundred feet she appeared small and a bit forlorn as she sat there, lifting her hand and nodding ten or fifteen feet above the people's heads.

Marcus drew an angry breath and turned away again, looked at his watch and found it was only eight-fifteen. Automatically, because it was expected of him, he tried a couple of sideshows. And automatically he found himself back near his car and lighting another cigarette.

The tent next to the structure of lilacs was in darkness and he guessed it was the one in which he and Sally would be expected to eat a supper of some sort with the *fiesta* officials. In there tables would already be loaded with cold chicken and salads, savories, fruit and nuts and dozens of bottles of wine. From the summit of the long tent a flag flew, looking happy and uncaring in the breeze. There was always a breeze for the Lilac Fiesta.

When a small flame licked up through the roof of the marquee Marcus couldn't believe his eyes. For a moment he thought they'd started sending up the rockets earlier than usual. And then the flame snaked out against the dark sky and was whipped down over the roof towards the lilac-covered erection. In a split second it flashed through his mind: a wooden framework filled in with bamboos and woven grass, covered with a thin material to which the flowers were fastened with adhesive and pegs. God! It would go up like paper. He raced across the grass towards the flames.

Though Sally had remained sitting up on high, raising her hand and inclining her head in the expected fashion, during the last eight or ten minutes she had felt distinctly uneasy. For out on the edge of the crowd which moved past a figure had stood quite still, staring up at her. The man was thickly built and dressed in the traditional way, and like about half the men here he was masked. She had made a point of not looking at him, but he had stood his ground, and finally she had to allow her glance to slide over him as she turned her head. And in that moment when their glances met he had touched his shoulder to make himself known to her, and made a warning sign with his hand; an urgent, dismissive sign. When she had looked again he was gone.

The man at Josef's cottage, she'd thought a little faintly. He hadn't left the island, had even had the temerity to come here and mingle with the merry-makers. What had he been trying to convey—his thanks in devil-may-care style? No, he hadn't been smiling, had looked grim in fact. Then what . . . ?

It was at that point that Sally heard shrieks and saw a lurid light reflected in the horror-struck faces of the crowd. Then suddenly one side of her bower was a glaring mass of heat and Marcus was just below, yelling with all the power of his lungs.

"Don't jump, Sally! I'm coming up!"

The policeman was frantically blowing his whistle, someone had already spurted away in a car to fetch fire-fighting gear . . . and Sally was crouched in one corner of the flaming structure while Marcus leapt from strut to strut till he reached her. With a roar, the fire engulfed the rest of the thing. Arms tight about her, he jumped, and took the fall with his side. Men jumped across them to kill the flames; the hushed crowd pressed forward.

Marcus was up on his knees, with one arm under Sally while the other hand thrust her hair back from her brow. Almost savagely he tossed away the coronet of lilacs.

"Get Dr. Suarez," he said thickly. "Quick!"

＊　　　　＊　　　　＊

It was so peaceful at Las Viñas that the next three days passed almost without Sally's being aware of the difference between night and day. The calf of her left leg had been blistered over a wide area and there were weals on her arms, but her face and hair had emerged unscathed—thanks to Marcus's swift thinking and wide protective chest.

The first day she had said to Carlos, "Is Marcus all right? Not hurt at all?"

"A cracked rib. He's fine otherwise."

After that she hadn't bothered about life very much. Marcus didn't come to her room to see her, but Katarina came in, looking oddly as though she might have been weeping. Viola, donning her brightest bedside manner, stated that the *fiesta* had been spoilt, of course, but there would be some other kind of high jinks to make up for it as soon as Sally was fit.

"And they're not sure that fire was an accident," she said chattily. "Peculiar things happened elsewhere that night, but we shan't know anything about it. That's the worst of these places. The most exciting things happen under cover. Are you comfy, darling?"

Sally was relieved when her mother drifted away.

On Wednesday, Carlos said he thought she had rested away all risk of shock and could get up for lunch.

"But eat up here in your balcony," he urged. "I predict that you will be very pleased to creep into bed occasionally for a rest."

"I think you're right. Has Doña Inez been told about all this?"

"Oh, yes. The second day, while you were sleeping, she came in here to see you." He smiled. "She did it all alone, too, because she suspected that Katarina had told her you were suffering from a burn or two as a sort of preliminary to worse news. She was terribly afraid that you were badly injured. So she came to see for herself."

Sally moistened pale lips. "I'll return the compliment as soon as I can look normal." She paused. "Is Marcus better?"

"Of course. There must have been pain in the rib for a while, but he said nothing. Each day I have reported to him about you."

"Is he . . . in bed?"

"But no! Yesterday he even drove his car." Carlos sighed, and raised his shoulders. "I will not try to deceive you. He is not happy — Marcus. You also are not happy —

I know that. I would like your permission to tell Marcus that you have asked for him and wish very much to see him."

"Thank you, Carlos," she said quickly, "but I'll deal with it myself."

He left it there. But the brief exchange with him had roused Sally from her lethargy. There was still the task she had set herself for last Sunday. She might steal a few more days, but in the long run they could do no more for her than had already been accomplished by the fire at the *fiesta* ground. Somehow that incident had estranged her completely from Marcus, and surely she had to be wise enough to take advantage of it. On the whole there was very little she had to say to him. Yes, the sooner it was said, the better.

She got up for several hours that day, but did not leave her room. On Friday, though, she half dressed after breakfast and slipped on a flowered housecoat. At about ten-thirty, she decided, she would put on a dress and go downstairs. And she would stay down there till she had seen Marcus.

For something to do, because she could not relax, she varnished her nails and walked into the balcony to dry them thoroughly. Someone had set the fountain playing in the centre of the pool; she could hear its cool rain and see a faint dampness where the wind had blown it. Idly she leaned out, and as she did so Marcus came up the steps from the drive and saw her. He stopped, just below. He looked a bit pale, but otherwise normal.

"How are you this morning?" he asked.

"Quite recovered, thank you," she said, and felt a new surge of fright. It was going to be terribly difficult.

"And the leg?"

"It's pretty good." She swallowed to dispel the huskiness from her tones, leaned forward. "Marcus, I want to speak to you."

"I'm glad," he said, and walked straight into the house.

Involuntarily, a fist came up and pressed hard against the base of her throat. What had he meant? That she should go down now and . . .

But he was there behind her in the bedroom, had come to the balcony doorway and was pushing one of the deep armchairs in front of him.

"Sit down," he said. "Carlos told me you were well, but you don't look it."

"You don't look quite . . . yourself, either."

"I'm all right." He saw her seated and himself sat on one of the balcony chairs. "I've just been down to the town. Several people sent their regards and best wishes."

"Thank you." Never in her life had she found it so difficult to articulate. "Carlos told me about your injury. Is it . . . mending nicely?"

"So well that I can't feel it."

"I'm so glad you weren't burned at all."

He smiled faintly. "My hair was singed and I'll never be able to wear that suit again. Perhaps it was a good thing I hadn't been drinking whisky."

Sally tried to smile back, but couldn't. "Do they know how the fire began?"

"It was arson — not to sabotage the *fiesta*, apparently, but to draw the police away from the coast. It seems that . . ."

"Before you go any further," she said in flat tones, "I'd better tell you something that . . . that happened . . . it must be a fortnight ago. You're going to dislike this, and I'm sorry I didn't tell you before, but . . ." her shoulders moved sadly, with resignation. "One morning — it was hardly light — Josef came here for me. He wakened me by tossing pebbles up here into the balcony, and begged me to go down to his house and help someone who was injured."

Marcus leaned forward, his eyes dark and narrow. "You went with him?"

She nodded. "We ran over the hill and the dunes. I found that the injury was a gunshot wound. As soon as it was dressed the man cleared off in a launch. I half thought it was a naval launch, but heard there were none missing."

"That was strategy. Two were missing." Marcus looked strained as he said, "You shouldn't have gone with Josef; you know that. It was dangerous and very foolish."

"I do know it now. Josef was tremendously relieved to get rid of the man and begged me to say nothing about him. I didn't make any promise, except that I did say I'd speak to him first if I felt it necessary to tell anyone; I've a feeling it's too late to bother with that now. I want you to know that if there'd been any enquiries I'd have told all I knew; as there was nothing said, I decided I'd been mistaken about the launch and that it must have been a poacher in the fishing grounds — something like that."

"You actually did it for Josef," he said. "Dressed the wound, kept silent about it, and so on?"

Something in his voice warned Sally to be a little careful. "I'd have done it for anyone in a fix. The point I wanted to make was that the man with the wound was at the *fiesta.* He made some kind of sign to me and then disappeared. Since I've had time to think about it, I've felt he was warning me to get away from that spot. He knew the marquee was going to be set alight."

Marcus said tautly, "You've been near to great danger, and not only from the fire. Through Josef too. You'd better realize that."

She looked at him then for a moment, and what she saw turned her heart. Averting her gaze, she said, "It must have been ghastly for you, seeing it all and having to act. I was dazed with the suddenness of it, and Carlos kept me under sedation for a couple of days, so it all seems a bit unreal now. Can you tell me what was at the back of it all?"

"It won't be made public, but I feel you should know. From the time when the first launch was missing the Navy had a committee looking into things. I represented the island on that committee, and knew all the moves they were making. It was decided that as Josef was the newest arrival on San Palos he should be watched." Marcus paused. "He didn't want the ceramics factory, you know. He wanted a cottage near the sea and a good reason for staying there; it was something he'd never done before, so it had to have an obvious explanation—like ceramics."

"But what *was* he doing in the cottage?"

"Making easy money. In his travels he'd met up with a man who handled the transport of displaced persons who had no passports. Their biggest problem was crossing the Mediterranean, and they solved it by picking on an island here and there and using some secluded bay till they were suspected, after which they cleared off. Josef had only been on the fringe of it, earning pin-money, but he was hard up, and when they needed a new base he recommended San Palos—which he knew intimately. Everything was done under cover of darkness; during the day, Josef tinkered with clay."

"Good heavens," she said soberly. "Who were these displaced people?"

"There are still a good many refugees about in Europe. Poorish, honest folk, most of them, though some of them do have enough money to buy a passage to a country where they could be swallowed up, unnoticed."

"But aren't there societies that help them?"

"They're long-winded, I suppose, and when a man hears that money will buy him something he's waited for for years, he gets hold of the cash somehow. This gang who have been handling the smuggling of men across different frontiers aren't fundamentally bad. To them it's an adventurous way of earning big money. When they let Josef team up with them, though, they showed a lamentable lack of judgment."

"Josef!" she whispered. "That wound on his head! And yet you can't imagine him doing desperate deeds for money."

"Exactly," said Marcus with irony. "He tried it, and failed. First he inadvertently holed the motor boat belonging to his companions and had to replace it. So, foolishly, he bribed someone to let him use a naval launch for one night. The launch was returned next day, and Josef, because there was no outcry, blissfully considered himself quite a

184

chap. But the man he was working with—a stranger on the island—had rather more about him. He could see that San Palos wasn't going to be the sinecure he'd thought, so he arranged a grand coup for the night of the Lilac Fiesta. While everyone was drawn by the *fiesta* and the fire to the east of the island, the west coast could be used for the landing of about a dozen people without passports."

"Are they here?"

"Not now. They've been sent to the mainland."

"You knew all about the plans?"

He nodded. "Josef's companions depended on him too much. He was picked up early that day and was frightened into confessing everything. After that it was easy to trap the others."

"And that man who'd been shot?"

Marcus shrugged. "He considered himself the swash-buckling hero type. He wanted money, but without harming anyone. That was why he set fire to an empty tent. It was only after all the plans were laid and he daren't back out that he realized how close you were to the blaze. That's why he tried to warn you."

"You've . . . spoken to him?"

Marcus's mouth was a straight line and his jaw muscles very prominent as he answered, "Yes. He was behind bars, or I'd have choked him." He touched her hand, just for a second. "Their game is up—let's forget them."

"But . . . but what's happened to Josef?"

"You still care what happens to him?" he asked abruptly. "All right, then, you'd better hear the rest. He's in custody, but he'll probably get away with a heavy fine. As you know, he detests me, and it's not likely he'll come back to the island. Don't feel sorry for him, for heaven's sake!"

She shook her head. "It's unhappiness that makes a man of his kind take to shady projects. He doesn't seem to belong anywhere. Is this his home—San Palos?"

"Yes, I suppose it is."

"He claimed you as a distant connection, but you said there's no relationship between you at all. Was he born here?"

He hesitated. "He's Katarina's son."

Sally felt her skin go cold and a little clammy as she took in the implications of his unembellished statement. "Poor Katarina," she murmured. "That explains such a lot. How is she taking this?"

He sat back abruptly. "She's had to do a bit of explaining, too. She was half aware of all that was going on, but daren't do anything about it. At first she tried to get Josef to give it up, but there were things he wanted, things she could never have given him herself—and the money was attractive. Against her will, she was persuaded to do some pretty low things."

"Such as . . . searching my room?"

"I'm afraid so; she told me about it herself. And you remember her telling me that she'd heard you and Josef conversing in the early hours one morning? Well, he and she arranged that between them."

"It's incredible," she said thinly. "She actually told you all this, without being asked?"

"I insisted that she tell me everything, and I think she did."

"But did she say *why* she and Josef went to so much trouble?" Why should he want to do so much against me?"

"It was more against me than you," Marcus said tersely. "The thing has quite a history. Josef is younger than I, but as boys we saw a good deal of each other. My grandmother had helped Katarina and she paid for Josef's education. It was Katarina herself who, when he was ten, insisted on his being told that she was his mother; before that, he'd imagined himself more or less adopted by our family. The truth must have been quite a blow, because almost at once he started going wild."

"And he drew a parallel between you and himself," said Sally slowly. "You were everything he wanted to be, and he considered himself rather less than every other boy. So he came to hate you."

"Maybe I could have been more tolerant, but it wouldn't have done any good because he would have regarded it as a kind of charity. Katarina had shown him his true relationship to our family and it shocked him into loathing everyone. You're probably right about his being unhappy, but even despair shouldn't drive a man into crime. I daresay he'd come to the conclusion that money was the answer to everything. How little he knew!"

This final exclamation left a brief silence behind it. Then, looking down at her hands, Sally said, "I think I understand about Josef now. Except that he and I . . . well, in a way we were quite good friends. Why should he want to act against me?"

"Josef couldn't be good friends with anyone," said Marcus sharply. "When he came here a year ago he ruined a romance simply because the man, someone he knew very well, was financially secure and very much in love. Luckily that particular case seems to be mending now. When he arrived this time he found that I'd become engaged, and I don't doubt that it put him into a rage of jealousy. Everything he did was calculated to break off things between us. He couldn't know, of course," with a faintly bitter edge to his tones, "that there was nothing very tangible to sever. Anyway, Katarina told me that she had to search your room for something . . . anything, that might give Josef a fact or two to work on. The first time she found nothing, but the second time she read some of your letters from England and discovered that I wasn't mentioned in any of them. Josef stored that in his mind; he said that if he could manage to see Doña Inez alone he would tell her."

"His whole idea," said Sally unsteadily, "seems to have been to make big money quickly and to shatter any happiness he might come across on his way. I pity him, very much."

"Maybe I'll come round to pitying him one day," Marcus said grimly, "but it isn't pity I feel for him now. He deserves whatever he gets. And now let's talk about something else." His manner changed. "You said you wanted to speak to me."

"Yes. Yes, I do, but you'll have to . . . to give me a moment."

His voice deepened. "Don't distress yourself, Sally. I'd rather wait a bit—even a few days."

"No, I have to say it soon, but all this about Josef and that man . . ."

"Yes, I know." He spoke steadily but gently. "I've something to tell you, too, and this may be a good time for it." An almost imperceptible pause. "I didn't go to Barcelona on business."

Her eyelids flickered, but her glance did not quite reach his face. She had to steel herself, so that whatever he'd decided about the future, she wouldn't give herself away.

"No?" she said politely.

"No!" There was rather more force behind the syllable than one might have thought necessary. "I went there to see Nadine Carmody. She sent me a telegram and I answered it in person. The next day I saw her off on a plane, and it's doubtful whether she and I will ever meet again."

"Oh, but you mustn't!" Sally cried, a catch in her voice. "We've taken this whole thing too far. Doña Inez isn't nearly so frail as she looks, and I happen to know that she wouldn't care a bit if I faded out and Miss Carmody came on to the scene. So long as an engagement exists she won't mind . . ."

He was standing, suddenly, and staring down at her. "What the blazes are you talking about? I don't want Nadine. There's only one thing in the whole world that I do want—and that's what I told Nadine when I met her. She was a flop in America—one generous mention in a small journal and silence from every other newspaper. She went on tour and couldn't take it, and so she decided to patch things up between us. But there was never any chance of that. Even if I hadn't met you, I wouldn't have married Nadine. We were never properly engaged . . ."

"But you were going to marry her."

He threw out a hand, almost irritably. "I went over to see her, with the possibility in mind. When I got there she was crazy about this chance in America, and I remember thinking, quite coldly, that that settled it, and that I was relieved. Nadine was good fun to take out, and as an antidote to the quiet life here the theatrical set was ideal. If Doña Inez hadn't kept badgering me to marry . . ." He broke off. Then he said, "I *had* to go over to Barcelona; it was the only way to deal with Nadine effectively and finally. She didn't like hearing that I was already engaged, but we parted amicably. She'll get another part, and find someone else. The Nadines of this world always do."

"But, Marcus," she said, hardly comprehending, "that was what I wanted to speak to you about. You see, I . . . I knew you went to see Nadine. Josef brought me a copy of her telegram."

"Good God," he said, and went pale with fury. "He really meant to tear us apart, didn't he? And when I got back you didn't say a word about it!"

"I was waiting till after the *fiesta*," she said tremulously. "I was going to tell you on Sunday morning. You see, I'd spoken to Doña Inez, sort of circled the point to find out as much as I could about her attitude towards me."

"So that's what she meant! Twice she's muttered something about having misunderstood how I felt and perhaps hurting you. Your narrow escape upset her badly, and on Sunday evening we found out that she'd come along to see you. After ensuring that you were sleeping normally she went a little lightheaded with relief."

"Oh, dear. One way and another I do seem to have caused a lot of trouble."

"That's not true. The only trouble you've caused has been through keeping things to yourself. And though that's the last thing I wanted to happen, it was probably my fault, because I knew just how vindictive Josef could be, and you didn't."

"And there was . . . Nadine," she reminded him.

"Since I've known you I've wondered why I ever bothered with Nadine. I hated even to hear you mention her. My feeling for you is so different from anything I've ever experienced before. It's real . . . and dammit, it's horribly painful!"

Sally didn't know how to answer that. She could feel a burning spot on each cheekbone and a nerve twitching in her lower lip; her brain was fuddled, but a sort of hazy hope shone through the haze. The kind of hope you daren't look at in case it vanishes.

She tried to speak objectively. "I've been as sensible as I could. It did seem that events had rather run away with you—first of all that McCartney man on the ship, and then your grandmother's precarious health. I was just a . . . an accidental fiancée, and you weren't in love with me—we weren't even close friends. And I thought . . ."

He took her shoulders and spoke down to her bent head. "From the first I liked you and rather enjoyed your mother. Viola must have told you that I meant to keep in close touch with you both. You'd been so shy and uneasy with me on the ship that I won't pretend I thought we might marry some day. At that time, I only knew I wanted to see you again. But when people assumed we were genuinely engaged I saw you differently — I saw the sort of woman you'd become once you felt secure and beloved. But it wasn't till I saw you and Carlos putting your heads together that I knew you were mine in every sense of the word. I was actually jealous of *Carlos*. It was a nasty experience, and I'm not over it even yet."

She lifted her head. "But, Marcus, you could have told me all this!"

"You wouldn't have believed. You'd have decided that I'm the type to tell the woman I intended to marry that I loved her; you'd have decided it was part of the code by which I lived." With a savage smile he added, "If I've learned little else about you, I'm pretty well up on the line your thoughts have taken about me. I think I've become familiar with the meaning of every turn of your head, every slightest change of tone." The hands tightened on her shoulders. "I can still feel right here in the tips of my fingers the way you shrank from me when I fastened the necklet for you."

She drew in her lip. "Well, I . . . I knew you couldn't have bought it for *me*. You can't get that sort of thing on San Palos."

There was a moment's electric silence. Then with harsh distinctness he said, "It was ordered from our family jeweller in Madrid. I described exactly what I wanted and they sent it. It arrived here only two days before I gave it to you." A long pause. Then: "I've been waiting a long time for the right moment to tell you I love you. I can't wait any longer — I want you too much. No more shrinking from me, Sally. I won't have it!"

Sally closed her eyes and leaned forward against him, and for a few seconds he held her that way, his arms tight about her. But inevitably his urgent lips sought hers.

It was quite some time later that she said, "Your rib must have healed remarkably quickly!"

"Oh, it hurts," he said, "but to hell with it. Physical pain is nothing at all compared to having your heart squeezed and twisted a dozen times a day. Each night since last Saturday I've lain in bed sweating back over those minutes when the flames were leaping round you, the way your skirt caught and flared."

"I was going to jump before the fire could reach me," she said.

"I know. I saw it in your face. In your panic, you might have cracked your head or broken limbs."

She said inadequately, "I haven't thanked you properly for saving me."

He laughed a little wryly. "When you save someone you love you save yourself. There's nothing brave about self-preservation. I haven't known you so very long, but there's one thing I'm sure of. Without you, I wouldn't want to live."

She looked into his eyes then, a little frightened. It was what she had wanted so desperately, to be loved like that; but it was a huge responsibility.

She said softly, "I've been childish in some ways, Marcus, but I do love you. I so longed to have you come in and see me. Why didn't you?"

"I did come in a few times, after you were down for the night, but I didn't want us to do any talking till you were up and thinking clearly. If I'd walked into your room each afternoon for tea, a new, polite little barrier would have grown up, because you wouldn't have been in a condition for frankness. The way I saw it, that *fiesta* fire had burned down part of the wall between us, and next time we talked the rest would have to crumble. As it has, my love!"

"Darling," she whispered, and put her arms about him.

His response was swift and passionate. Sally didn't want to think any more for a long time. Some time she would get down to musing about Katarina, who must be helped out of her sadness; of her mother, who would no doubt prefer Captain Northwick to Mr. Essler. Perhaps some day soon she and Marcus could find out which of the nurses in the British section of the nursing home had attracted Dr. Carlos Suarez; they must have some social meeting ground . . . and what better place than Las Viñas?

Las Viñas, the home that Sally and Marcus would share for the rest of their lives.

THE END